"Who are you in love with now?"

The warmth of Damon's lovemaking suddenly ebbed away as Rachel remembered why he was doing this. A basis for comparison, he had said, proof that almost any man could make her love him by rousing her normal sexual impulses.

"Don't look so murderous, Rachel," he continued mockingly. "You should be thanking me for a lesson in loving."

"Loving?" she said scornfully. "It was a lesson in lust, wasn't it? Well, thank you for making me feel cheap and dirty with your demonstration!"

"Oh, God," he exclaimed. "I should have known better than to kiss a child."

"I'm not a child and you know it," she said furiously. "And I'm going home." She swallowed back tears, determined to be adult about this if it killed her!

The Jasmine Bride

by

DAPHNE CLAIR

Harlequin Books

TORONTO • LONDON • NEW YORK • AMSTERDAM
SYDNEY • HAMBURG • PARIS • STOCKHOLM

Original hardcover edition published in 1979
by Mills & Boon Limited

ISBN 0-373-02329-4

Harlequin edition published May 1980

CHAPTER ONE

SHE had often swum in the little cove. It was entirely secluded except for the small house which perched, less precariously than it appeared, on the brow of the steep slope above the beach.

The day was beautiful, and the lazily breaking waves looked inviting. The red car, that incongruously smart and slick vehicle that had been parked for days beside the weatherbeaten little house, its shiny paint and brash chrome shaming the greyed boards and peeling corrugated iron roof of the building, was missing. It had been there this morning, she knew.

He must have gone to town. It was over fifty miles to travel, and could take up to two hours over the dusty metalled road, winding in and out of the valleys and over the sheep-sprinkled hills, and crawling through the gorge where the native bush tumbled in wild abandon to the occasional glitter of a stream on the valley floor. The road was narrower than ever there, and in winter it sometimes fell away into the gorge, cutting off the sheep stations from the rest of the world until the weather cleared and the Ministry of Works sent a bulldozer to carve new curves from the reluctant hillside.

It was too much to hope that some freak of weather and wind would provide a convenient landslide today and like the careless hand of Tane, Maori god of the forest, sweep aside the red car and its occupant, removing them from her life for ever.

He was a townie, Rachel thought, her mouth moving in a contemptuous curve—a city man. Even on a lovely clear day like this, inexperience of backblocks roads and perhaps city-bred impatience and over-confidence might combine to spell disaster for such a man. But no, she told herself with bitter resignation. He was probably scared stiff and fussily steering his car with slow caution through the gorge, afraid to risk his lilywhite, civilised neck.

She turned away from the house and again looked longingly at the blue water, the curving line of the breakers tempting her like an insistent, beckoning siren call. Sea and sky blended perfectly on the horizon.

She had no swimsuit, and Auntie Anne would be horrified at the idea of her swimming without one ...

She glanced again at the house on the hilltop, wondering if she dared——

Perhaps he had gone for good. He might have found a week of being alone and away from it all too much for his taste, after all. His whim might have played itself out already, and he was retreating back to the bright lights and the noise and the sophisticated, rather artificial society of the suburban intelligentsia described in his books.

Book, Rachel reminded herself, for she had read only one of his works, and it had left her with no desire to read another.

The sun was hot on her fair head, and a sudden glint of it off the rolling sea dazzled her eyes. She walked a few yards down the sand, mesmerised by the inexorable movement of the waves, the headlong rush to shore suddenly muted to a loving caress of the sand as the water slid gently over it and withdrew reluctantly, leaving bubbles of foam behind in gentle curves.

Suddenly impatient of restrictions and conventions, she stripped off the faded knitted cotton shirt she wore, then the old jeans that she had really outgrown, and the cotton panties beneath, and threw them one by one up the beach on to the heated sand, throwing back her head to catch the sun on her closed eyes as she ran into the water.

It was everything it had promised to be, exhilarating with the first cold shock, and then warming into welcome as she let herself be taken into its rough embrace, the breakers playing with her, throwing fine spray into her face and lifting her over their crests, carrying her shoreward when she turned and rode on them, her naked body straight and taut, taking her by surprise as she turned and dived under them.

She could have stayed for hours, but time and conscience intervened and after about half an hour she reluctantly headed for the shore, riding one last wave before she stood, the sand under her feet sinking and the water pulling against her thighs as it receded. Her hair clung wetly to her face and shoulders, and she pulled it away from her eyes, bending her head to gather it into a heavy hank and wring out some of the water.

When she lifted her head and saw the man standing on the sand and watching her, the shock kept her still for a second or two. Then instinctively she lowered her hands in the age-old futile gesture of feminine modesty.

There was a long moment when she thought he wasn't going to move at all. Then he slowly turned around and stood, hands on his lean hips clad in dark jeans, his blue-shirted back firmly turned, but equally firmly not moving away.

She kept her eyes painfully fixed on his back as she moved cautiously out of the water and up the beach to gather her scattered clothing. He was standing only a few yards further up, but he didn't seem to move at all as she hastily pulled her panties and shirt on over her wet skin and with some difficulty got back into her too-tight jeans.

'Let me know when you're covered, Aphrodite,' he said, making her jerk up her head, but he hadn't turned.

She didn't want to talk to him. Fervently she wished she had taken notice of Auntie Anne. She glanced round at the headland that enclosed the cove, but the tide was much too far in, leaving her no hope of scrambling round the rocks. The only way was up the path past the house, and *he* was in the way. Still, she was a fast runner, and he was only a townie, after all, probably not used to exercise. If she took him by surprise——

She swerved past him with the speed of a rabbit, but he came after her and caught her with a hard hand on her wrist before she reached the path.

She twisted her imprisoned wrist outwards and down to break his hold, but the infallible trick failed for once. He merely shifted his grip slightly and hauled her closer, capturing the other wrist as he did so.

Held like that, it was useless to struggle. He was much stronger than she had expected, and although her own slight figure and slim wrists and ankles belied her healthy vitality, she knew she had no chance against him.

He looked implacable, too. He had dark hair, a bit untidy and longish—by local standards, anyway. Where he came from long hair was probably the norm. His face was a trifle craggy and worldworn, with an aggressive cast about the chin and a stubborn mouth. Light grey eyes, chilly as a morning sky, were inspecting her with a sort of detached curiosity, taking note of her dishevelled, water-darkened hair and defiant sea-green eyes, slipping over her mouth, faintly parted with the quickened tempo of her breathing, lingering on her shirt where it clung damply over sharply defined breasts.

Embarrassed, she lowered her own eyes to his chest where his shirt was open to the second button, showing lightly tanned skin with a faint covering of dark hair.

'You're only a child—dressed,' he said, bringing her eyes flying back to his face. The implacable look had faded and he looked rather amused.

'I'm sorry if you're disappointed, Mr Curtis,' she said, with no forethought at all, her tone decidedly tart.

Surprise replaced the amusement just for an instant, then he threw back his head and laughed, loosening his grip so that she was able to free herself and leap away up the path.

She knew he was right behind her, and when he caught her arm at the top of the slope she knew he had let her stay ahead only from choice.

'Don't run away,' he said quite mildly. 'I want to talk to you.'

'I'm not running away,' she lied, because if she didn't know he was capable of holding her there at his pleasure she would have been off and away across the paddocks as soon as he released her arm. 'I don't happen to feel like talking to *you*,' she added.

'That sounds pretty personal,' he commented, his eyes narrowing on her face. 'What have I done?'

'Nothing,' she said quickly, then contradicting herself, 'For one thing, I don't like being spied on.'

'I wasn't spying,' he said, the grip on her arm tightening with his anger. 'Has it occurred to *you* that you were trespassing?'

'*Trespassing?* Oh, you—If anyone's a trespasser here it's you! I have more right to be here than anyone—I *told* them they shouldn't have let you have it, but it was too late!'

Her inarticulate rage and pain brought a puzzled look to the grey eyes, and his hand became quite gentle on her arm.

'Who are you?' he asked, his eyes intent now on her face.

'Rachel Standen,' she said bleakly. 'I used to live here'— her eyes went to the house behind him—'with my father.'

It was obvious the name meant nothing to him. The expression in his eyes didn't change as he gently slid his hand down her arm to her wrist.

'Well—' he said. 'Come inside, Rachel, and tell me all about it. I'd like to hear.'

'No!' she said sharply. She pulled away, and his fingers slid down a little more to enfold hers, then clamped tight.

'Are you always so rude?' he enquired mildly, but there was a faint spark of annoyance in his silvery eyes.

'Sorry,' she said, looking down sulkily. 'I mean—I can't, thank you. Anyway,' she added, ingenuously struck by the perfect excuse, 'I'm not supposed to go anywhere with strange men.'

'I'm not a child molester!' he protested, apparently struggling between vexation and mirth.

'Well, *I'm* not a child!' she cried, unreasonably annoyed with him because she realised how childish her remark had been. 'I'm eighteen—nearly. Over the age of consent.'

His expression changed suddenly, becoming cynical and faintly damning. 'I'm delighted to hear it,' he said silkily. 'Is that an invitation?'

Around a sudden frightened fluttering in her throat she said, trying to invest the words with some dignity, 'Certainly not. I thought I'd been making it quite clear I don't like you.'

'That doesn't always have a lot to do with it,' he said. 'But you won't have found that out yet. Anyway,' he insisted, suddenly impatient, 'come inside. You may be legally old enough, but I'm on the other side of thirty, and I can promise you your immature charms won't tempt me to lay a finger on you.'

She didn't have much choice, because he was still holding her hand, and he led her to the door and opened it, giving her a little push when she hesitated.

She walked into the centre of the small front room which faced the sea, and looked about as he closed the door behind them.

The faded carpet was still on the floor, but there were several sheepskin rugs scattered round the room, and the old three-piece suite had been augmented by several large cushions and a comfortable-looking recliner chair. A plain table near the window held a typewriter and two stacks of paper, a basket file and a couple of folders.

'I thought you were on holiday,' she said.

'Writers don't have them. If I was parted from my typewriter I'd be a candidate for the lunatic asylum within a week. Would you like a cold drink? There's Coke, lemon and paeroa, or orange cordial.'

'I'll have cordial, please,' she said, half relieved, half annoyed that he hadn't offered her the choice of something alcoholic.

She wandered to the kitchen doorway after him, watching as he took a jug of cordial from the small refrigerator in one corner and poured out two glasses from it.

Thinking he didn't look like a teetotaller, and wondering if he was having cordial only to keep her company, she said as she took one of the glasses from him, 'If you want something stronger, I don't mind.'

'Thank you,' he said. 'But I don't have anything stronger in the place. I didn't bring any with me.'

'Oh, I see,' she said vaguely, wondering if that was the reason he was here, remembering some of the things she had read about writers and artistic people in general.

'What a busy little brain you have,' he said gently mocking. 'No, I'm not drying out, Rachel. Drinking is a social pastime, and I'm not often in need of alcohol when I'm on my own. Sit down.'

He waved her to the sofa and took a chair himself, leaning back and watching her as she sipped her drink.

'So you used to live here,' he said.

'My father practically rebuilt this house. It was almost a ruin.'

'Really?' He glanced around, perhaps impressed. It wasn't a glamorous or modern house, but it was sturdy and cosy, and in spite of its shabby outward appearance, quite weatherproof still. 'Is your father a builder by trade?'

Rachel shook her head. 'A jack of all trades, he used to call himself. He's dead now.'

'I'm sorry. Why did he rebuild the house?'

'For me. I was four when he came here to work for Uncle Bert—Mr Langholm. It was a temporary job at first, then he sort of stayed on—there's always work for a jack of all trades about the station. We were living in a little caravan then, but Auntie Anne said it was unsuitable for a little girl—she wanted me to live in the house with them, but Dad said no. This place was empty and just about falling down, and he asked if he could have it. He told me he wanted me to know who my family was, and he was it. There were only the two of us.'

'What happened to your mother?'

'She died when I was very little. I don't remember her at all.'

'And how long is it since your father died?' he asked gently, his eyes resting curiously on her downcast face.

'Three years now. I was fourteen when he—there was an accident with a tractor. It rolled on him.'

'I'm sorry. That must have been tough, at that age.'

Rachel lifted her left shoulder a little. 'I suppose it's always tough, at any age.'

'True. I was twenty-five when both my parents died in a car crash. I have a sister, but it wasn't easy for us, either. Not so bad as being orphaned at fourteen, though. Are Mr and Mrs Langholm really your uncle and aunt?'

'No. They've been very kind. Their own children have all left home now, except Jerry—he helps on the farm. Auntie Anne insisted on having me, because they couldn't trace any relations of my father. She was very patient with me. At first I kept coming back here, insisting I could live here on my own. I guess I was a bit hysterical,' she finished, shamefacedly.

'Not surprising, in the circumstances,' He paused, then said, 'I take it you're still sensitive about having someone living in your old home.'

She looked at him with faint apology. He was being quite nice, and perhaps she *had* been a bit unreasonable. The Langholms, anyway, certainly thought so.

'Well, you see,' she explained, 'I always thought of it as *our* house—I mean, my father died without making a will, but there wasn't much anyway. I just thought of this as our home. But it belongs to the Langholm land—there was no lease or anything, he just asked if he could have it, and Uncle Bert said yes. There was no legal agreement or anything, so I suppose, although my father almost made a new house of it, it belongs to the owner of the land.'

'You may have some legal claim. Have you thought of getting a lawyer?'

'Oh, *no!* I couldn't—there's no need for that. I was a bit upset that they rented it to you without asking me—I felt I had a right to be consulted, you see. But even if I had, they're entitled to the rent. They've had all the expense of keeping me for the last three—nearly four—years. So even if it *is* my home, I owe them that, you see.'

'Did they tell you that?' He frowned.

'They didn't need to. I know how much they've done for me. They're very good people.'

They *were* good people, of that she was convinced. If sometimes she felt misunderstood and hurt, it was more her fault than theirs, for she was well aware that they tried hard, and only refused to accommodate her wayward moods because an over-sensitive nature would betray her if it wasn't sometimes curbed. Auntie Anne's obvious disapproval of what her father had 'let her get up to' was never put into words. In the face of Rachel's inevitable adolescent cries of '*Dad* let me do it!' she was both firm and tactful. 'You're not a little girl any more. He wouldn't let you do it now.' And if she suspected that her father would have been less rigid, less insistent on her learning the domestic arts and how to behave like a 'decent girl,' there was no court of appeal, for he was dead and except for Anne and Bert Langholm, she was on her own.

Damon Curtis stood up and put his empty glass on the square coffee table that stood between them.

'So you knew,' he said, 'that I rented the place. I thought when I saw you down there that you couldn't have heard—whoever you were.'

She looked up and saw the speculation in his eyes and was stirred to anger. 'You were out!' she said indignantly. 'Your car was gone.'

'It was surely on the cards that I'd come back,' he pointed out reasonably. 'You took a risk, didn't you?'

'I didn't expect you back so soon! There's only one place you can go from here, and I thought you'd be in town for the whole day.'

'Why on earth should you think that? It only takes a little over an hour and a half to get there. I finished my business in less than an hour and came back.'

'You went there for just an *hour?*' Rachel exclaimed.

'I'd not a great deal to do there, I'm afraid.' He smiled. 'I assure you an hour is all it took me to replenish a few supplies and post some mail.'

'Well, I wasn't to know that,' said Rachel. 'When we go to town, we spend the day!'

'Well, I didn't rent a place in the back of beyond so that I could fritter away my days shopping.'

'Why did you?' she asked, curious.

'To work. On a very special project that didn't seem to jell when I was constantly being interrupted by telephone calls and well-meaning friends, plus my own weakness for a certain amount of social life.'

'Is it another novel?' Rachel asked.

'Yes. Am I flattering myself in deducing that you've read some of my work—or at least heard of it?'

Of course she had; he was one of New Zealand's better known novelists.

'Of course I know who you are. I did recognise your name. There was quite a lot of publicity when you sold the film rights of your last book.' She paused, and as he seemed to be waiting for her to go on, she said, 'I read *Bread of Deceit.*'

'And—?'

'I didn't like it,' she said clearly, meeting his eyes with bravery.

'Thank you,' he said, and she thought he was being sarcastic, but he added quietly, 'for telling the truth.'

She stood up, saying, 'Auntie Anne will be looking for me. I must go.'

'Perhaps you'll like my new book better,' he said. 'I'll send you a copy when it's published.'

'Thank you.'

He came to the door with her and said, 'If you feel like swimming again, I may join you. Knock on the door when you come—if you don't mind company.'

'I don't mind,' she said. She hoped he realised that if she did swim again in the bay she would be wearing a suit. She hesitated, wondering if she should make that clear, decided against it and walked quickly away.

CHAPTER TWO

SHE managed to reach her own room unseen and change out of her still damp clothes into a dress, and dry out her hair before the time came to help prepare the evening meal. She would have preferred to be outside, working out on the hills with Jerry and his father, but Auntie Anne had strong views on the role of women, and although there were times when she would don rubber boots and help with a will when her husband was short-handed or the stock threatened by some natural disaster, the provision of meals was strictly a female affair, and not to be shirked. It had never been quite clear to Rachel why the station work was hard and wearing for the men, making it necessary for them to be fed hearty meals at regular intervals, and to be looked after by their womenfolk in every possible way, while if *she* did it, the same work was frivolous indulgence, an excuse to escape from her 'real' work of domestic chores.

But it was no use arguing about it, so she set to, peeling potatoes and kumaras with deft if absent-minded movements, and going out to the neat, carefully weeded well sprayed and dusted garden that Anne kept at the back of the house, to gather an armful of silver beet.

She washed it, watching the water flowing over the dark green crinkles of the leaves, making them heavy in her hands before she shook off the moisture and put them aside to be chopped. The flowing water on her fingers awoke a small echo of the waves washing over her in the cove, before she had come to shore and seen Damon Curtis watching her.

Aphrodite, he had called her, joking she supposed, in reference to his seeing her rising from the sea, like the

15

Greek goddess of legend. But she was no goddess of love, as he implied with some amusement when he saw her dressed and called her a child.

Her face warmed with the memory, and she attacked the silver beet with a sharp knife rather savagely.

'Be careful, Rachel—you'll cut yourself!' her foster mother admonished, pausing with an egg in her hand, ready to crack it open on the edge of a stainless steel mixing bowl.

Rachel flashed her a quick smile and was careful, slowing her impetuous movements and making an effort to concentrate on what she was doing. She was especially amenable that evening, rising from the table to clear it almost before the family finished eating and volunteering to help Anne to darn the thick woollen socks the men wore with their work boots, instead of curling up into one of the big old armchairs with a book. She had a faintly guilty conscience to appease, and somewhere in the back of her mind lurked a vague idea that if she was especially good, a merciful providence might ensure that Auntie Anne never learned of her escapade of this afternoon.

The television was showing a sports programme, and the two men were absorbed in watching it. But once when a commercial break interrupted the replay of an international tennis match, she glanced up and found Jerry's eyes resting on her with an odd look.

He looked away immediately, and Rachel returned her attention to her darning. But a few minutes later she felt that he was looking at her again, and she raised her eyes rather reluctantly to confirm it. This time the blue eyes across the room held hers quite deliberately, with a look in them that produced a strange sensation somewhere in her midriff, a mixture of fear and excitement. Her cheeks were suddenly on fire, and she bent her head fiercely over the sock stretched across her knuckles, jabbing the long darning needle in the wool with a force that grazed her skin.

It was the first time she had seen desire in a man's eyes, and yet instinctively she recognised it. A primitive female triumph mingled with uncertainty in her emotions. Her confused mind flew back to Damon Curtis with some sense of vindication—he had called her a child, but here was proof of her womanhood. But at the same time her secure little world tipped to a dangerous angle on its precarious axis, and she glanced at her adopted aunt and uncle with a more sharp sense of her own essentially extraneous place in their lives—an orphan taken in from kindness, without any claim of blood or even natural affinity. In this house there were no long talks about the infinities of the world such as she had just begun to enjoy with her father before he died, no shared moments of joy over a poem, a sunset or the perfection of a tiny shell washed up on the beach.

Her uninhibited appreciation of such things, once the first passionate storms of grief subsided, had been met with blank lack of understanding, with firm and kindly admonitions to 'be sensible,' and sometimes with less kindly male teasing from Jerry, the youngest son of her adopted family, but six years older than herself.

Most of the time, at first, he had simply ignored her. Later, when he had got used to her presence, she supposed that he treated her like a kid sister. She had never had a big brother so had no basis of comparison.

He casually accepted the small services which his mother had taught Rachel to render him as a man, the cups of tea delivered to his elbow and collected when he had finished with them, the mended shirts and socks, the cold beer taken out over the paddocks on hot days, the bedmaking and tidying up that she did for him.

And in return he sometimes took from her a load of wood for the winter fire that had her struggling, and once she was sixteen and deemed old enough for some social life, had rather reluctantly consented sometimes to take her to local dances, where he left her at the doorway and at the end of the evening collected her again with a laconic, 'C'mon, let's go.'

She supposed he was quite good looking, with his blue eyes and sun-bleached hair, and a healthy tan on a compact, muscular body. Looking at him now that he had turned back to the TV and was watching the finale of the tennis match, she remembered that he seemed popular at the dances. The local girls of the district were never reluctant to dance with him, although he was no more than competent in the art.

The match was finished, and over the music of a commercial Bert turned to his wife and said, 'Saw our tenant today.'

Rachel's breathing quickened with nervousness, as she wondered if Damon Curtis had given her away. But surely, if he had, Uncle Bert would have mentioned it before now? Yes—he would have told Auntie Anne and left it to her to 'straighten out' their wayward ward.

'How is he managing?' Anne found it difficult to believe that any man could 'manage' a house of whatever size on his own, and was slightly huffy about the Curtis man anyway, since he had refused an invitation to have a meal with them some time, and made it clear that he didn't want to be too friendly with his landlords. In the backblocks hospitality was a byword, and to have it refused, however politely, was something of a slight.

'He's all right, so he says,' said Bert. 'He was going into town for groceries.'

'He could have asked me, if he was out of anything, instead of going all the way to town.'

'Told him that. He didn't take much notice. Independent sort of bloke, I reckon. Said he wouldn't want to bother you, and it was no problem to drive into town.'

'It wouldn't be any bother,' Anne said with vexation. 'These townies have no idea—I'll pop down there tomorrow and see him, I think.'

'Think that's a good idea?' her husband enquired mildly.

'Well, it can't do any harm.'

'You won't be welcome. Think he's a bit of a Greta Garbo type, myself. You know he told us he didn't come here for the social life. If you ask me, he'd rather be left alone.'

'If you ask *me*, he's probably regretting he was adamant about it, and was too embarrassed to come and ask us for a pound of butter or whatever it was he needed.'

Listening to the conversation, Rachel tensed. Uncle Bert had met the man before he went into town—before her escapade. What if he decided to tell her aunt about it? He seemed to think she was only a child, and might take it on himself to mention her nude swim to her guardian. She would have to try and see him before her aunt got a chance, and persuade him not to give her away.

Quietly she folded the socks she had been darning and put away her needle and wool in the old-fashioned sewing box that stood in a corner.

Looking up, Anne said, 'Would you make coffee, dear?'

She went out to the kitchen and made three cups of coffee to put on the tray and carry back to the sitting room. She didn't feel like sitting there and drinking coffee herself. She wanted to go to her room and think . . .

She gave a cup to Bert and placed another on the table at Anne's elbow. As she carried the third cup to Jerry, she knew he was watching her, and when she handed it to him their fingers touched. He smiled at her and said, 'Thanks, Rachel.' His eyes still followed her as he lifted the cup and she turned away from him.

The room suddenly felt stifling, and she said abruptly, 'I'm going to bed. Goodnight, everyone.'

She closed the door of her own room with a strange sensation of having escaped from something.

She flung off her clothes and carelessly threw them on the bentwood chair in the corner, rummaged under her pillow for the cotton nightie and quickly wriggled into it. With her hand on the doorknob, ready to go to the bathroom, she paused. There was a lemon quilted nylon brunch coat hung on a hook behind the door. Anne had bought it for her last Christmas, but she only used it in the winter, to keep warm. Now some barely understood instinct prompted her to put it on, pulling the edges together as she opened the door and went down the passageway to the bathroom.

When she emerged from it ten minutes later it was

to see Jerry coming out of the sitting room, his empty cup in his hands.

Seeing her, he turned and looked at her, holding the cup towards her. 'I want another one,' he said.

He was perfectly capable of getting his second cup of coffee himself, and no doubt had been on his way to do it when he had noticed her. But nearly four years of Anne's training was strong, and she didn't want to annoy Jerry, so she went towards him and took the cup from his hand.

He followed her into the kitchen, watching as she boiled some more water and put a spoonful of instant coffee into the cup. The jug was boiling, and Jerry moved up behind her, switching it off at the wall, dropping a casual arm about her shoulder as he did so. He kept it there while she poured water over the coffee and stirred it. When she moved away, pushing the cup towards him, his hand slid down her back to her waist over the nylon padding before he picked up the cup, glancing sideways at her as he did so.

Rachel edged past him and made for the door, murmuring a stifled goodnight.

She woke very early in the morning and lay waiting for the hands of the small clock by her bed to reach six o'clock. She dressed very quietly in a sweater and jeans and crept out of the house and into the cool morning air. The coarse grass was prickly under her bare feet as she darted across it into the shelter of some dark, shaggy macrocarpa trees that would screen her from the house, and then found the narrow sheep-track that would lead her to the bay.

She hoped Damon Curtis was an early riser. She would have to get back before seven or her absence would be noticed.

When she arrived at the old house there was no answer to her knock, even when she positively thundered on the door. She opened it and called, with no result, and she didn't quite dare to go in and disturb him in his bed.

Sighing with exasperation, she turned away, and down on the beach a small patch of colour caught her eye—it could have been an orange towel lying on the sand.

Hopefully, she scanned the rolling surf, and just as she saw a dark blob among the white-caps, he unmistakably raised an arm and waved.

Rachel took off at a run, and by the time she reached the sand, he was wading out of the water to meet her. She scooped up the towel and handed it to him as he reached her, water dripping from his dark hair and running down his chest and legs. He was slightly tanned all over, wearing dark blue swim shorts that fitted snugly enough to emphasise his male physique.

'So—history reverses itself,' he said, grey eyes laughing as he took the towel from her and roughly dried his hair, chest and arms with it. Tucking it round his waist, he added, 'Just as well I didn't yield to the temptation to follow your example. What are you doing about so early?'

'I wanted to talk to you,' she said. 'About—that. Auntie Anne is coming to see you today.'

'Oh—why?' he asked sharply. 'What have you been telling her?'

'Nothing!' Rachel cried. 'That's the whole point. I'm hoping you won't either—that's what I came to ask you. Would you please not tell her about me? I mean, that I swam without anything on.'

'Why on earth should I? If *you* haven't mentioned it, I'm hardly likely to tell on you, am I?'

'I don't know,' she said. 'I thought you might think you should tell her.'

'Did you?' He looked slightly perplexed, a little amused, and she realised he didn't think the incident at all important, and thought she was making a mountain out of a molehill.

Feeling a little foolish, she tried to explain. 'Auntie Anne is sort of funny about things like that,' she said. 'I mean—she'd make a terrible fuss.'

'Would she beat you?'

'Oh, *no!*'

'What, then?'

He seemed really to want to know, and she said, 'Well, she'd talk a lot about decency and modesty and—the kind of girl I'm likely to grow into if I do things like that. That sort of thing. She's really very nice—but she does go on a bit, if you know what I mean.'

'I think so.' He took her hand and began to walk up the beach to the path. 'Did you tell her that you'd met me?'

'No.' That sounded as though she had been deliberately secretive. 'I would have had to explain how, you see.'

'Yes, I see that,' he answered. 'Well, when she comes to see me, I won't let on that I know you at all, then. Why *is* she coming, by the way, if it's not to beard the wolf in his den?'

Rachel felt a bit uncomfortable about asking him to be secretive, but it seemed the only way, so she answered his question, letting the first remark pass. 'She just wanted to make sure you don't go all the way to town every time you run out of something. Uncle Bert told her you went yesterday.'

He looked slightly annoyed, and as they reached to top of the path he dropped her hand and swept back his damp hair. 'I thought I'd made it clear I don't want to play Good Neighbours. Your Aunt Anne is very kind and no doubt means well, but I just want a place that I can rent and be left alone!'

'Yes, you did make it clear,' said Rachel. 'They told me about it when you came—that you didn't want to have any social contact with the district, and wouldn't accept any invitations. But she thinks you could be having second thoughts, since you're used to the city ...'

'I'm not having second thoughts!' he said irritably. 'I don't change my mind every week like a blasted weather-vane.'

'Then—perhaps you didn't mean it, yesterday, when you said you might like to swim with me?'

'That's not a social engagement!' he said. 'Of course I meant it. Not going all hurt on me, are you?'

Rachel shook her head, but reminded herself that she

mustn't take him up on the invitation too often. 'I'd better get back,' she said. 'She'll probably invite you again to come and have a meal with us. I don't suppose you'll come?'

'I don't suppose so, either,' he said, and she made to turn away, but he caught at her hand and asked, 'Do you want me to come?'

She looked up into his cool grey eyes with surprise and said, 'Please yourself. Auntie Anne will be disappointed if you don't.'

'Will she?' He sounded very dry, and the look in his eyes made her uncomfortable. She tugged at her hand and he let it go.

'I'll see you, then,' she said carelessly and he said, 'Yes,' and stood watching her as she scampered away along the path.

Mrs Langholm returned triumphant from her errand. Mr Curtis had not only received her politely but had accepted her invitation to have dinner with them the following evening.

'Roast lamb with peas and mint sauce,' she said. 'And I'll make a pavlova.' It was hardly an original menu, but she was a superb cook who invested plain fare with a gourmet's touch, and as she said, there was nothing like home-killed meat and home-grown vegetables.

Rachel found that she was nervous, and on the following evening, after helping to prepare the meal, she stood in front of her wardrobe and surveyed its not very extensive contents with unusual disfavour. She would have to wear a dress, since they were having a guest, but she had a sudden passionate desire for something sophisticated and striking that would make her look like a very adult sort of person—and there was nothing among the mostly home-made garments hanging there that would even begin to fulfil that desire.

She tried a pretty cotton sun frock against her, looking critically at its crisp young freshness, the rounded neck-line and the bodice trimmed with white broderie anglaise.

Impatiently she discarded it, and hauled out a navy silk shirtwaister that Auntie Anne had bought at a sale, and which she hardly ever wore. She put it on, daringly leaving the top two buttons open—it didn't really *show* anything, but it did give it a certain sophistication, and when she pulled the belt fairly tight and slipped her tanned feet into a wedge-heeled pair of white leather mules that had been given to her as cast-offs by Anne's eldest daughter, the effect was faintly like what she was looking for.

She tied up her hair in a high ponytail, then rummaged in her drawer until she found some bobby pins, and after a good deal of trial and error managed to produce a firm, reasonably sleek chignon.

Anne only allowed the palest of lipsticks, and most of the time Rachel didn't bother with it, anyway, but tonight she used it carefully, and wished she had some eye make-up to darken the fine bleached ends of her lashes and emphasise their length.

She emerged from her room just as there was a knock on the front door. Anne came out of the kitchen, untying her apron, and casting a quick, critical glance at Rachel, snapped 'Do up your buttons!' before she went to the door.

Mortified, Rachel obeyed, and stood awkwardly with her hands loosely clasped together as Anne ushered Damon Curtis into the wide hall.

'This is Rachel, our adopted daughter,' she heard her say, and she glanced up briefly, taking his proffered hand as he murmured, 'Hello, Rachel.' His fingers felt warm and firm, and she realised that he had a very pleasant voice, deeply masculine and without a hint of harshness.

They went into the lounge and he was introduced to Jerry, who muttered an inarticulate greeting and then buried his nose deeply in a glass of beer.

Damon accepted a whisky from Bert, who then poured a glass of sherry for his wife.

Rachel, without giving herself time to think, said coolly, 'May I have one, too, please, Uncle Bert?'

He looked at her in surprise and she felt herself flushing, wishing she had kept quiet rather than risk being reprimanded like a child in front of their guest. Then Anne said calmly, 'Yes, give her one, Bert. Rachel's quite old enough now for a small sherry with the family.'

Her cheeks still felt hot as she took it from him, and she bent her head and sipped quickly from the glass. Then she flashed a grateful glance at Anne, but she was talking to Damon Curtis, and he had his head turned away from Rachel, concentrating on the conversation.

When she had finished the sherry she felt a little drowsy, but she followed Anne to the kitchen when the older woman went to dish up, and by the time she had eaten her roast lamb followed by the light, delicious pavlova topped with rounds of green kiwi fruit, she felt very much more alert.

Their visitor was not doing a lot of talking—his conversation consisted mostly of questions, and he was getting Bert to tell him quite a lot about the work of the sheep station and the problems of farming life. Rachel couldn't remember ever hearing Bert talk so much.

When they went back to the lounge with their coffee, Damon Curtis turned to Jerry and began skilfully to overcome his reluctance to carry on a conversation by discovering his interest in rugby football and asking more leading questions.

The two women gathered up the coffee cups and washed the dishes, returning to the lounge to find the three men having a spirited argument about rugby tactics.

Or that was how it appeared at first. Rachel seated herself on a hassock in a corner and watched the dark man who sat back in his chair, cool eyes moving from the older man to the younger one as they leaned forward towards each other, Jerry pounding the air with a clenched fist to emphasise a point, and Bert waving his pipe as he contradicted his son. Damon Curtis interjected every now and then with a brief remark, and Rachel was reminded of a person tending a fire, casually throwing the occasional twig on to the flames to keep them burning.

He raised his eyes and met her faintly critical stare, giving her a slight, enquiring smile.

Rachel didn't return the smile. Some of the hostility she had felt for him before she had even met the man had returned. She didn't think she liked the way he stayed detached and observant while he manipulated her adopted family. He had already charmed Auntie Anne out of her slight annoyance with him by his notably good manners, standing when she entered the room and taking the tray of cups from her, and telling her her cooking was superb.

He strolled over now and sat casually on the arm of the sofa, where Anne sat knitting, and she moved her pattern and ball of wool to make room for him beside her.

'Don't bother,' he said. 'I'm fine here. I like old-fashioned furniture—it's somewhat more comfortable than most modern stuff.'

Anne smiled up at him and murmured something and began counting stitches.

His foot was almost touching Rachel's. His shoes were well polished but had picked up some dirt—he had evidently walked over, and she wondered a little maliciously how he would manage on the uneven unsealed road or the sheep-track short cut on the way back in the dark.

His foot shifted a little and she knew he was looking down at her.

'Have you finished school?' he asked.

'I never went to school,' she said.

'Rachel had correspondence lessons,' Anne told him. 'She has just had her university entrance exam accredited by the Correspondence School.'

'Will you be going to university Rachel?'

She shrugged her shoulders, still refusing to look at him.

Anne answered for her. 'Rachel hasn't decided yet what she wants to do. We think it would be a good idea for her to stay with us for a year or so, and have a break from schooling and exams. Then, if she wants to get a job, or go to university—although there'll be problems in that case'— she sighed and shook her head gently. 'Personally I think it's rather a waste of time for a girl, but it seems her father wanted——' she shrugged.

Rachel smiled to herself. 'He said I should get a degree so that I could treat it with the contempt that it deserves,' she said, glancing a slightly challenging look up at Damon Curtis.

'Did your father have a degree?' he asked, apparently interested.

'Oh, yes—I think so.' She was staring at his shoes again, wishing she had not given him that small glimpse into her father's character. She was suspicious of his interest. She wondered if he was taking mental notes, his detached writer's eye dissecting them all as he had dissected the characters in *Bread of Deceit*. He had a cruel pen.

'What subjects are you interested in studying?' he asked.

Indifferently, she answered, 'I don't know. Maybe history —English literature—perhaps anthropology.'

Auntie Anne made a small, exasperated sound, and said, 'Of course, teacher training might be more useful.'

With a small, depressed smile, Rachel said, 'Yes.' She was well aware that Anne despised her father's ideas on education and the upbringing of daughters, although she had too much respect for the fifth commandment, and too much common sense in dealing with children, to ever say so outright. Rachel knew that the suggested year at home while she 'made up her mind' was supposed to help her come to a sensible decision about her future. And Anne's idea of a sensible decision was to either find work in town until one of the local farmers' sons decided to ask her to marry him, or to learn teaching so that she could support herself before marriage and be of some use to her children and the community afterwards.

'Aren't you interested in teaching?' asked the man at her side. Rachel, suddenly feeling crowded, not only by his nearness but the reminder of the year ahead of her, said, 'I'm thinking about it,' and stood up.

She went over to the record player, saying, 'Can we have some music, Auntie Anne?'

'Not too loud, dear,' was the reply, and she smiled

acquiescence and began looking through the pile of records on one of the speakers.

Jerry got up and joined her, and after they had selected a long-playing disc of Latin-American tunes, she sat on the floor in front of his chair, leaning against it with her shoulders touching his knee.

Across the room, Damon Curtis was talking to Auntie Anne, but looking at Rachel. Without meeting his eyes, she could feel them assessing her, making her skin prickle with tension.

'Your hair's coming down,' said Jerry, and she felt his finger against her neck, picking up a wayward strand and tugging on it gently. She put up her hand, encountering his fingers before he dropped them, and twisted to smile at him as she pulled out a pin and readjusted it to hold the errant lock.

His blue eyes were warm as he smiled back, but when she turned away it was to see cold grey ones across the room, speculative and strangely disquieting in their intentness.

She was relieved when finally their guest stood up and, refusing more coffee, took his leave. She stood up to say goodnight to him, and Jerry, after a disapproving look from his mother, got awkwardly to his feet, too.

Damon Curtis stopped in front of her and said, 'Mrs Langholm tells me you used to swim quite often in the bay in front of my house, Rachel. Don't let me stop you. Why don't you come tomorrow?'

He was smiling, with a teasing glint in his eyes, noting her faint alarm at his bringing up the subject at all.

'Thank you,' she said, castigating him with her eyes while trying to smile unconcernedly.

His own smile broadened just a fraction before he turned away and was escorted to the door by his host.

CHAPTER THREE

RACHEL didn't go to the cove the next day, nor the next. She had a curious reluctance to meet Damon Curtis again.

But on the following Sunday she was sitting in the shade of a grey-trunked karaka, scribbling with a stub of pencil in a small notebook, when she heard his voice behind her.

'What are you doing?'

'Nothing,' she said instantly, quickly closing the book and pocketing it in her denim shorts.

After a moment, he asked, 'May I join you?'

'If you like,' she said, gazing away from him over the gentle swells of the paddocks with the distant glimpse of sea beyond.

He hesitated a moment before lowering himself to lean against the smooth bark of the karaka, his shoulder almost touching hers.

They sat in silence for a time, and she began to accept his presence. Then, quietly, he said, 'This is beautiful country. You're lucky to have been brought up here, in one of the most unspoilt areas of New Zealand.'

'Where were you brought up?' she asked, suddenly curious.

'Mostly in Wellington,' he answered, and smiled when she shuddered.

'I hate cold and wind,' she said.

'Don't you ever get cold and windy days in Hawkes Bay?' he asked.

'Yes, but Wellington is like that all the time, isn't it?'

'Not at all. Have you ever been there?'

'I've never been further than Napier; not since I was four, and I don't remember before that.'

29

'Do you mean you've never seen a bigger city than Napier?'

She met his curious look with defiance. 'I don't specially want to. I don't much like what I see on TV and read in the paper about them.'

He smiled. 'It isn't that bad. If you go to university, or want to train for teaching, you'll have to go to a city, won't you?'

'Yes, but ...' She paused, then said, 'I like the idea of Auckland. It's warm, and close to the sea.'

'Think you'd feel more at home there?'

Rachel nodded. 'If I get there,' she said tensely.

'Why not? You want to go, don't you?'

She turned away with a troubled look, gazing at the far blue of the sea, and he said gently, 'Scared?'

'No!' she denied sharply.

He didn't contradict her, but said, 'Before I leave, I'll give you my address, and phone number. Maybe you'll look me up. Do you have any friends in Auckland?'

She shook her head. 'Is that where you live?'

'Yes. I'll show you round when you come, if you like.'

'Thank you.'

Firm fingers suddenly closed on her smooth chin and turned her face so that he could look at her. 'Still resenting me for living in your house, Rachel?' he asked.

She pushed his hand away and said, 'No, of course not.'

'You haven't been swimming lately.'

'I haven't had time.'

'Do they keep you so busy, Cinderella?'

'I'm not a Cinderella!' Rachel said vehemently. 'They've been awfully kind to me.'

'Yes, I know,' he said reflectively. 'It's possible to kill with kindness.'

'That's stupid!' Rachel got swiftly to her feet, repeating, 'That's a *stupid* thing to say.'

She would have flounced off, but he was blocking her way, having risen just as swiftly as she. He put his hands on her shoulders and said softly, but with warning in his eyes, 'I'm not stupid, Rachel. But if I've offended you, I'm sorry. No doubt I should mind my own business, but believe me, I was only trying to be—friendly.'

She looked at him uncomprehending, and moved her shoulders so that his hands dropped.

'How about a swim?' he suggested, smiling at her. 'I haven't been in today, and the water looks perfect.'

Suddenly the thought was overpoweringly attractive, and she wondered why she had denied herself for so long. 'I'll have to go back to the house and get a suit,' she said, and flickered her eyes away from his as he smiled with obvious meaning, eyebrows slightly raised.

'I'll wait for you,' he said. 'Or shall I come with you and ask your aunt's permission?'

'That isn't necessary,' she said, turning away.

A few steps away she turned and said, 'Jerry might like to come. Is that all right?'

There was a moment's silence before he said, 'Sure. Bring him along.'

Rachel didn't, because Jerry and his father were watching an international sports telecast, each with a large glass of beer in one hand and a cigarette in the other, and she knew it was useless even to suggest a change of entertainment.

She pulled on her low-backed one-piece swimsuit, wrapped a comb and ribbon into a big towel and dropped a towelling shift cover-up over her head and slipped out again.

When she came out near the big karaka, Damon Curtis was sprawled at its foot, hands cradling his head, and she thought he had gone to sleep, until she came close and found the grey eyes lazily watching her. He didn't move when she came to stand beside him, but lay there just looking at her, taking in her long tanned legs and the short shift with the tie belt at her narrow young waist, and moving up to her face with sleepy interest.

He smiled at her and reached up a hand. 'Like to help me up?' he invited.

Catching his teasing mood, Rachel poked her bare brown foot gently into his ribs and said, 'Get up yourself, lazy!'

She was moving away when he rolled over and grabbed at her retreating ankle, bringing her tumbling on to the soft turf as she lost her towel.

She rolled over and raised herself on her elbows, to find him beside her, his hands planted on either side of her so that she couldn't get up.

'*Now!*' he muttered, his eyes glinting. 'What was that you called me?'

'Nothing, Mr Curtis!' she said, her heart beating fast. They were playing, she knew, but there was something deeper underlying the play and the teasing. She smiled at him, biting her lip at the same time.

His eyebrows rose a fraction, and he said, '*Mr* Curtis? How old do you think I am, Rachel?'

'I—don't know,' she answered. 'But you told me that you're too old for my—my *immature charms* to tempt you.'

'So I did,' he drawled, his eyes moving along her supine body to her bare toes and back to her face in a long, slow scrutiny. The look in them had changed to something warmer and altogether more disturbing. Wryly he said, 'Supposing I was wrong, Rachel—does that scare you?'

It did, but there was a sensual excitement in it too, and she was suddenly very aware of the texture of his skin with its light tan, the strength of the arms that imprisoned without touching her, the firm male beauty of his mouth.

She parted her lips to answer him, and licked them with the tip of her tongue because they felt suddenly dry. Then she said softly, 'No.'

He held her eyes a moment longer with his, then he smiled and said tolerantly, 'Yes, it does. You're a witch, Rachel, but a very young one.'

He moved back and stood up, pulling her to her feet.

She picked up her towel and carefully re-rolled it, feeling distinctly anti-climactic, keeping her eyes on her task.

Damon Curtis's voice said behind her, 'Don't be disappointed, Rachel. You're quite beautiful, and I'd have to be made of wood not to appreciate that, but only a—well, the old-fashioned word is cad, I suppose—would take advantage of such—inexperience. I should have known better than to tease you.'

'I'm not disappointed, she said. 'I said I wasn't scared. That didn't mean I wanted you to kiss me.'

'No,' he said after a moment. 'Of course not.'

Rachel stood fiddling with the end of the towel, and he said, 'Shall we have that swim?'

She shrugged and started off along the grass and a few seconds later he was beside her, hands casually in his pockets, his face expressing nothing but pleasure in the sea-borne breeze that ruffled the hair that fell across his forehead, and the warmth of the sun glinting off the waves as they neared the bay.

He went into the house to change and by the time he emerged she was waist-deep in the water, hardly waiting for him before she struck out strongly into the welcoming breakers.

Later he lay on his towel on the hot sand, watching her as she combed out her hair.

'You should have a rock to sit on,' he murmured.

She smiled and said, 'I can't sing.'

'All mermaids can sing.'

'And lure men to their deaths,' she said. 'I'm not a mermaid.'

'You swim like one. You're very good.'

'My father taught me very young,' she explained.

'Swimming—and what else?'

'Reading,' she said. 'Everything—until Auntie Anne and the Correspondence School took over.'

She put the comb down and rolled over on her stomach, sifting sand through her fingers until there were only a dozen or so fine grains in her palm. She separated them with her fingernail, seeing that each one was different in shape and colour, watching the sun catch them.

'What are you thinking about?' he asked.

'The sand,' she said. 'All along the beach, these millions of grains, and each one is different.'

He didn't answer, and she dusted the sand off her palm,

feeling silly, and depressed as well. She folded her arms and put her head on them, facing away from him.

Then he said, 'You're right—so they are.' And she turned her head in his direction and saw him staring into his palm as she had done. He looked at her and smiled, and for the first time since her father had died she recognised a moment of joy with another human being, and felt tears begin to form in her eyes.

Hastily she buried her face in her sun-warmed arms, but he must have noticed. A gentle hand grasped her shoulder and turned her over on her back. His face, looking down at her, was puzzled and concerned as his finger touched her cheek at the corner of her eye.

'What is it?' he asked.

She tried to smile, and said, 'Nothing. Just—you reminded me of my father. I've been lonely since he died.'

His expression was rather rueful, but he said, 'I suspect that's the nicest thing you could have said to me. Also that I haven't a hope of living up to it.'

He moved a little away from her and leaned on his elbow, still looking at her. 'Were you a happy child, before he died? Weren't you lonely then?'

'Not really. There were a couple of Maori families here —I used to play with the children, and Auntie Anne rounded us all up for correspondence lessons at the house, with the mothers taking turns to supervise. But they've all gone away to find work. And my father had a lot of books. I still have them. They take up two walls in my room— Uncle Bert built shelves for me.'

'So you're a reader. What do you like to read?'

'Most things. My father had a lot of books on natural history, and a collection of English classics.'

'Which you've read, of course.'

'Most of them.'

Looking interested, he said, 'Let me guess. You loved the Brontes, of course.'

'Emily and Charlotte, yes. I thought Anne was rather peevish.'

'Dickens?'

'Some. I like *Great Expectations*.'

'Jane Austen?'

'Not really. She's so—*genteel*.'

He laughed. 'Wait until you're old enough to appreciate her. Charlotte Brontë didn't like her books either.'

'Really?' Intrigued, Rachel sat up, staring at him. 'I didn't know that!'

'There's a lot you don't know, isn't there? You'd better go to university and learn some of it.'

Undecided, she looked down at the sand and said, 'Maybe.'

She didn't want to talk about it, and apparently realising it, he asked, 'Have you read many novels?'

'A few.' She looked at him briefly with a small smile. 'Yours for one.'

'*Bread of Deceit*, which you didn't like.'

She looked up again and shrugged, and he sat up, his forearm resting on his knees, and said, 'Tell me why.'

She shook her head, and he said, lightly, 'It wasn't too genteel, was it?'

She laughed, and said, 'No.' Then she looked pensive and added, 'But if Jane Austen had been a man, she might have written something like it.'

After a moment he said, 'How very flattering of you, Rachel. And how perceptive.'

She looked into his eyes then, and found the courage to say soberly, 'It was cruel.'

His eyes looked very silvery in the sunlight, and his face was quite impassive. 'It was honest,' he said.

'Was it?' She had to believe him, but a little shiver started up her spine as she remembered the selfish, self-deceiving characters that peopled the book, the small every-day brutalities they had practised on each other. 'Do the people you know act like that?'

'The people I *created* acted like that,' he corrected her.

'You mean you made them up completely? They weren't based on real people?' She was a little relieved at that, but she searched his face, wondering how he could invent people like that.

'They weren't very nice,' she said, and he laughed.

'And you think that *I* can't be very nice, too, don't you?' He lay back again on the sand, cradling his hands behind his head. 'One of the things about creating a novel and inventing the characters,' he said, 'is that you really don't *know* where they come from, who they're based on, if anyone. At least, that's how it is for me. I lost a—good friend, over that book. I couldn't convince her that I hadn't based the character of Karina on her.'

'Karina was pretty dreadful,' Rachel remembered.

'Karina was a right bitch,' Damon agreed. 'The lady in question—wasn't. Or maybe she was, and my subconscious recognised it and translated her into Karina in my book. She certainly gave a good impersonation of Karina the day she walked out on me.'

As the sense of that remark penetrated, Rachel realised what he probably meant, and glanced at him, then quickly away.

'Yes, we were lovers,' he said, answering the unspoken question. 'Does that shock you?'

Rachel shook her head, not looking at him again, and he said, 'No, I suppose not. It fits in with your idea of the dissolute life of a writer, no doubt.'

That made her angry, and she looked directly into his mocking eyes and retorted, 'You're the one who's jumping to conclusions.'

He raised an eyebrow and said, 'Perhaps you're right. It must be those clear green eyes of yours, awaking my dormant conscience.

'I don't know what you're talking about,' she said.

'Don't you? Well, look on it as a compliment,' he said, making that impossible by the satirical note in his voice. 'I keep forgetting how young you are.'

'I wish you wouldn't harp on it,' she said rather sharply.

'Believe me, you should be grateful.'

She looked away, her mouth a trifle sulky, and he laughed. 'Don't look so downcast. I'm actually doing my damnedest to be kind to you.'

'You needn't bother,' she said, and reached for her shift,

pulling it over her head. 'It's time I went home, anyway.'

Damon watched her as she knelt on the sand, tying her belt, and didn't move. But when she was going to get up, he shot out a hand and grasped her wrist. 'Come again,' he said.

She didn't answer straight away, but he held her wrist until she gave a nod of assent. Then he released her and said, 'Tomorrow?'

'Maybe.' She shrugged. She was busy rolling up her towel, and when she looked at him again he was regarding her with a rather cynical little smile on his lips.

'Well, I don't *know!*' she said impatiently. 'It depends on Auntie Anne, you see. I can't promise.'

He lifted his eyebrows, and then the smile changed to a real one, and the cool eyes warmed a little.

'All right,' he said lazily. 'I acquit you of coquetry—you haven't the experience for it, have you? Although it seems to come naturally to some women.'

'I'm not one of those,' she told him shortly.

'Oh, I'm not sure of that—Aphrodite,' he said. 'But whatever you are, it comes naturally. You're not the type to indulge in cheap tricks.'

She cast a look at him that made it clear what she thought of that idea, and he laughed softly.

Rachel pushed her loose hair back from her face and wondered vaguely what had happened to her ribbon. Perhaps she had lost it in the water.

'What's the matter?' Damon asked.

'My hair-ribbon,' she said. 'I've lost it.'

'Have you? You had it on when you came out of the sea—I saw you pull it off before you combed out your hair.'

'Did I? It must be under your towel, then.'

He got up and lifted his towel, and scooped to pick up the scrap of scarlet before she could reach it.

'Turn around,' he said, standing with it in his hand.

After a moment's hesitation she obeyed, and his fingers touched the skin of her nape and shoulders as he gathered up her sun-dried hair into his hands and tied it tightly with the ribbon.

'There,' he said, and just for a fleeting moment his hand rested on the curve of her neck and shoulder, his thumb moving in a light caressing movement over the top of her spine.

She said, 'Thank you,' rather shakily, and moved away, full of disturbing emotions that were brand-new to her experience. She smiled in his general direction, calling what she hoped sounded like a careless goodbye, and made for the pathway.

When she reached the top she looked back down at the beach.

Damon was lying prone, his head on his arms, dark hair contrasting with the dark gold of the sand. Rachel stood there for some minutes, but he didn't look up, and eventually she turned and made her way slowly back to the homestead, trying to think rational thoughts and put her newly awakened feelings into order.

Damon Curtis was an attractive man, and an experienced one. It was fairly obvious he found her attractive, too, and she couldn't suppress a faint excitement at the thought. But he also made it clear that she was little more than a child in his eyes, and that was how he was determined to treat her.

There was a definite temptation to prove him wrong, to see if he was, after all, able to resist what he had called her immature charms. That did rankle a little.

But neither her father's nor Anne's upbringing had included any encouragement to deliberately use her feminine attractions on any man simply to prove their potency.

And besides, it would undoubtedly be playing with fire. If he succumbed at all, it would probably be only because no women of the kind he was more used to happened to be available in this backblocks retreat he had chosen. When summer ended he would leave, and find someone older and altogether more like his style.

That she wasn't his style, she didn't doubt for a minute.

For his girl-friend to walk out on him because of it, there must have been some resemblance between her and Karina, the fictional character in his book. And Karina had been depicted as a very sleek lady indeed.

CHAPTER FOUR

RACHEL didn't have to decide whether to visit Damon or not, because Auntie Anne sent her over on Tuesday afternoon with a half dozen eggs laid by her own hens.

'Tell him they're extra, and going to be wasted if he can't use them,' she said.

Knowing it wasn't true, Rachel promised to deliver the message with the eggs and asked, 'Can I have a swim while I'm there?'

'Well—I suppose so. You won't be a nuisance for Mr Curtis, will you?'

'I won't.'

She saw him before she knocked on the door, because he was typing at the table near the window. She thought at first he was going to ignore her, because he went on typing rather fast, but after a minute he raised a hand without looking up, and she deduced he meant her to wait.

Eventually he pushed back his chair and shouted, 'Come in!' And when she pushed open the door he was coming to meet her. He looked a little distracted, so Rachel said quickly, 'I didn't mean to disturb you,' and gave him the message and the eggs rather hurriedly.

'Thank you, Rachel,' he said, turning towards the kitchen. 'Don't go,' he added, as she took a step to the still-open door.

She stopped, and waited while he put away the eggs and came back into the room.

'Are you swimming?' he asked, glancing at the towel under her arm. 'May I join you?'

'You're working,' she said. 'Aren't you?'

'I've just finished a chapter,' he said. 'Hence the intense

concentration a moment ago. I could do with a break before starting on the next.'

'Oh—well, I'll see you down there, then.'

She went out and ran down the path to the sand, and stripped off the shorts and tee-shirt she wore. She tied up her hair and stood waiting impatiently until Damon appeared outside the house.

He had a very nice body, she thought, as she watched him coming down the path. Long legs and narrow hips, and he looked masculine without being over-muscled.

He reached her side and looked at her without the faintest flicker of the sexual awareness he had shown last time they had been together.

'Race you to the water,' he said, and of course he did, because he didn't give her a start. He was a good swimmer, too, and she had to admit that, townie or not, he wasn't soft or stupid.

She dived under a wave and started as something pale and long with floating tendrils appeared beneath her. It took only a moment to realise that it was only a rock, smooth and white, and a trail of brown seaweed attached, but it had momentarily looked like a girl down there, and she surfaced, gasping, and turned on her back to float and recover her composure.

Damon was beside her, 'Something wrong?'

She shook her head and laughed a little. 'I thought I was seeing Pania,' she said.

For a moment he looked quite blank, then he gave her a sceptical look and dived under the water, coming up again to smile at her quizzically.

'She's there, all right,' he said. 'Isn't she rather a long way from home? Napier is miles further down the coast.'

As they lay on the beach, drying out after their swim,' he said, 'I'm hazy about the details of the Pania legend. It's rather like Hans Andersen's Little Mermaid, isn't it?'

'Pania was one of the sea-people, and she used to swim ashore each evening to watch the local people come to the spring at the foot of the Hukarere cliff.'

'And she fell in love with a handsome young prince— '

'Chief.'

'Chief, then. What was his name?'

'Karitoki. He saw her one day, hiding among the flax by the spring, and he fell in love with her and took her to his house to be his wife. They were very happy, but each day the sea-people called and called to Pania to return to them, and to her home. And she knew that if she did, she would never be able to return to her husband, whom she loved so much.'

'Yet eventually she yielded.'

'Only because Karitoki cheated her.'

'I didn't know that. How did he cheat her?'

'Pania had a child by Karitoki, a boy named Moremore. And then she was able to visit her people each day, because as long as she left the boy with her husband, the sea-people would let her go back to her child each evening. But Karitoki was worried in case Moremore should take it into his head to follow his mother, and the sea-people would keep them both. So he went to a *tohunga* for advice, and the *tohunga* told him to place cooked food on the bodies of Pania and Moremore while they slept, and then they could never return to the sea.'

Damon smiled. 'Not a very romantic spell, surely? I'm not surprised it didn't work. What happened then?'

'When Pania woke up and discovered what her husband had done, she didn't reproach him, but gave him a sad look, picked up her child and walked into the sea. Her people met her and surrounded her and drew her down to the depths of the sea, and she was never again allowed to come to the surface and see the land where she had been happy with her husband.'

'And today, on a clear, calm day, Pania can be seen beneath the waters of the harbour at Napier,' Damon said quietly.

'Yes—with her arms stretched in longing towards the land and her lover, and her long hair streaming in the current. The Maoris say Rawaru the rock cod live cradled within her left arm, Tamaru the schnapper are found in the crook of her right arm, and Hapuku the groper swim between her thighs.'

Damon was smiling. 'You know, as a writer, I envy the man with the imagination to concoct that story about a seaweed-covered reef.'

'It's a beautiful story, isn't it?'

'Yes, it is, and it has an interesting theme—the girl torn between her love for her husband and her love of her people and her home, her own element. And there's a beautiful irony in the fact that she left her own husband because he wanted so much to keep her that he deceived her and tried to hold her by trickery.' Thoughtfully, he said, 'I could use that theme . . .'

'In a book?'

'Maybe. But I must finish the one I'm working on first.'

'What is the theme of the one you're working on now?'

'Loneliness. Or self-sufficiency, depending on which way you look at it. It's about a man who loses everything and everyone he relies on or holds dear, and he has to fend for himself—a sort of modern Robinson Crusoe, although his isolation is from choice rather than an Act of God, as in Crusoe's case.'

'Is that why you came here to write it—to get the feeling of isolation?'

'Exactly. But I'm not quite such a hermit as my protagonist in the book. He buys himself a block of land that's still covered in bush, builds a cabin with no mod cons at all, and proceeds to make like a pioneer.'

'It sounds interesting. And not much like *Bread of Deceit*.'

'It isn't a bit like *Bread of Deceit*. This is about a man finding himself.'

'Whereas that was about people who had lost themselves.'

'That's a very mature comment for a person of your age.'

'And that's a very condescending comment for one of *your* age!'

Damon laughed. He looked very nice when he laughed. It took away the slightly world-weary look he often wore, and made him look young and carefree.

'You can't be all *that* old!' she commented watching him.

'Thirty-three,' he said. 'And you're seventeen.'

He said that almost as though it faintly disgusted him, and she told him defensively, 'I'm eighteen next week.'

'Are you indeed? Will there be a celebration?'

'Nothing special,' she said. 'Just a sort of family party. Would you like to come?'

'Thank you, I'd be delighted.'

He didn't sound delighted, more like polite and not particularly interested.

'If you'd rather not——' she began.

Damon cast her an impatient look and said, 'Don't be silly.' Then he pointed out to sea and asked, 'What's that fellow?'

Rachel watched the huge bird flapping clumsily over the surface of the water, then taking off with rapid wingbeats before going into a high glide in a wide circle.

'It's a gannet,' she said. 'They nest on that little island out there.' She pointed to a small barren island beyond the the headland.

'Impressive, isn't he?' Damon murmured. 'His wing span must be all of five or six feet.'

The bird was still flying in wide circles, and coming quite close to the beach. It seemed to pause momentarily in the air, and then with wings half-folded dived into the breakers, and emerged some seconds later with something glittering in its beak. A few quick shakes of the bird's head, and the glitter disappeared. The gannet bobbed on the waves for a while, then took off again in its ponderous, slow-beating fashion, ending in the glorious, graceful flight, white feathers gleaming against the blue of the sky.

'He's got his dinner,' said Damon.

Rachel grimaced, 'Poor fish!'

'That's nature's way. Do you want the gannet to starve?'

'You don't have to tell me about nature. I was brought up on this station, remember.'

'So you were.' He looked at her with a faint smile. 'But

your environment isn't the woolshed and the high hills. The sea people call to you, don't they, as they did to Pania?'

She smiled and said nothing, but it was true. All her life had been lived within sight and sound of the sea, and it was quite likely that if taken away inland, she would pine and mourn for it like Pania.

Damon came to her birthday tea, bringing a glossy, perfect shell, a spiral cream speckled with brown spots, the inside of it a delicate shiny pink; and a spray of manuka flowers, their white petals centred with the same faint blush of pink.

'I haven't been to town,' he said, 'so I haven't bought a present for you. But I found this the other day, and thought you might like it.' He smiled and added, 'I suppose you have dozens.'

'No,' she said. 'Perfect ones are very rare. Usually the tip is missing, at least, when they're washed up on the beach. Thank you—I love it.'

She put it in the centre of the table with water in it, and broke off some manuka flowers to arrange in it.

There were two parcels by her plate. Usually Anne bought something and wrote a card with three names on it, but this year there was a separate one from Jerry. The card that lay on top of it featured a glossy photograph of three voracious-looking purple orchids, all open throats and stiffly curled petals, and the gold writing that curled across it proclaimed 'A Happy Birthday to a Very Special Girl.' The verse inside was rather dreadful, too, and Anne insisted that Rachel read it out.

Rachel did so in as steady a voice as she could muster, and looked up to see Damon raise a hand to hide a twitching mouth, and Jerry gazing fixedly at the table.

She put down the card and hastily opened the package that went with it, shaking out the folds of a satin scarf printed with a design of full-blown pink roses and sprays of violets, and revealing a pair of extremely fluffy pink mules, nestled in the box underneath it.

'Mum said you needed slippers,' Jerry explained. 'She told me the size.'

'Oh, yes, I do!' Rachel assured him, avoiding Damon's eyes. 'They're—they're awfully glamorous. And the scarf, too. Thank you very much, Jerry.'

She was touched to think he had gone to the trouble of buying them for her, and seeing a gleam of laughter in Damon's eyes, she was suddenly angry with him. Jerry was sitting next to her at the table, and she leaned over and kissed his cheek, before turning to open the second package.

'For your chest,' Anne said kindly, as Rachel withdrew the dainty china cups and saucers from their wrappings and put them down beside her place. There was a set of silver spoons, too, with a rose pattern to match the roses on the cups. 'You're old enough to start one, now.'

'Roses all the way,' Damon murmured, deadpan.

And Anne smiled and said, 'Yes, they're always nice, aren't they?'

'Very nice,' Damon agreed, and raised an eyebrow in Rachel's direction as she sent him an angry glance.

'Put them away now, dear, and we'll eat,' said Anne.

Rachel obeyed quickly, bundling the things back in their boxes and taking them to her room while the older woman began serving the meal.

After they had eaten they sat in the lounge, Damon on the sofa beside Anne, and Bert and Jerry taking the two easy chairs.

Rachel eyed the hassock in the corner by Damon, and elected to perch on the arm of the sofa on the other side of Anne. That way it was practically impossible for Damon to talk to her, and most of the conversation was between the two older Langholms and him. Jerry, never a sparkling conversationalist, spent the greater part of the evening reading the sports section of the paper.

Damon rose to leave quite early, and Anne said, 'See Mr Curtis to the door, Rachel. He's *your* guest tonight.'

She led the way in silence, going on to the small wooden porch with him only because his hand on her arm lightly compelled her. There was jasmine growing around the wooden posts that supported the porch, starry white blossoms scenting the night air. There were pale stars in the sky, too, and the air was clear and warm.

'Thank you for inviting me, Rachel. I enjoyed myself.'

'Yes, you did, didn't you?'

In the light spilling from the hallway he looked at her piercingly. 'You're angry with me—I thought you were.' When she didn't answer he asked, 'Why?'

She turned her shoulder on him and made to return inside, but he wouldn't allow that. He caught her upper arms and turned her to face him.

'Are you annoyed because I didn't buy you a proper present?' he asked her.

'No, of course not. It was the nicest of the lot——' she looked up at him accusingly. 'But you didn't have to sneer at the others.'

'I didn't sneer!' he snapped, frowning.

'You were laughing!' she said.

'Give me credit!' he objected. 'I was doing my darndest not to, as a matter of fact.'

'I don't see what's so funny about my presents.'

'Don't tell lies,' he said calmly. 'You could hardly keep a straight face, reading that ghastly verse.'

'Well it *was* a ghastly verse,' she admitted candidly. 'But——'

'And you're not an orchids and roses type,' he said. 'I admit my sense of humour threatened to get the better of me when I saw those slippers.'

'It was sweet of Jerry to buy them for me,' she insisted. 'He's never given me a present of his own before. They may not be smart or—sophisticated, but they're fond of me, and it isn't their fault if I don't appreciate what they——' she halted, then stumbled on. 'It isn't funny!'

Looking into her wide eyes, he said soberly, 'No, come to think of it, it's rather tragic. They have never given you anything you really wanted, have they?'

He was looking down at her with something like compassion in his eyes, and she knew that this man whom she had known a few weeks understood her better than the people she had lived with for the past four years. *He* would have known instinctively that she would rather not have pink bedroom slippers or rose-covered tea-cups for her 'chest.'

Her eyes stung suddenly, and Damon muttered softly, 'Oh, God!' and pulled her into his arms, his hand behind her head holding her face close to his jacket as his lips pressed a long, soft kiss against her temple.

'Poor little mermaid, you don't belong among the land-folk, do you?' he murmured, his fingers stroking her hair.

Being in his arms felt very safe and comfortable, and she sighed a little as she leaned against him, wishing it could last.

He took a deep breath, that she felt as well as heard, and held her away from him. His light eyes had darkened, and his smile was rather twisted, a little disconcerting.

She was looking up at him, questioningly, but one of his hands moved to come under her chin, tipping her face up further as he studied it.

'Well—you're eighteen now,' he said. 'Old enough for this, anyway.'

His bent head blotted out the light, and she closed her eyes as his lips met hers with a firm but fleeting pressure.

'Not orchids and roses,' he said softly as he lifted her head, still holding her and looking into her slowly opening eyes. 'Wild honeysuckle, and jasmine. Manuka that stands against the sea-winds and bears fragile flowers on slender, tough branches. I'll never give you roses.'

He released her so suddenly that she instinctively put out a hand behind her, although she was in no danger of falling. Cool blossoms sprayed from between her fingers as they clutched on a hanging raceme of jasmine; spent petals clung to her dress and fell softly at her feet.

'Goodnight, birthday girl,' said Damon, and went away from her down the dark path.

Rachel slowly uncurled her hand from the jasmine and went inside the house. But the perfume clung subtly to her fingers and she could still smell it later as she undressed for bed.

CHAPTER FIVE

MUSTERING was under way again. Rachel watched from the kitchen doorway as a mob of sheep flowed down the hillside in a small white tide, skirting the bracken-filled gully, urged on in their blind downhill panic by the dogs and men behind and about them. A ragged edge showed in the tight white mass as one or two tried to break away, but a distant whistle alerted a dog, and in a quick, streaking flash of black-and-tawny speed, the renegades were headed off and forced back into the mob.

Within minutes the mob had reached the flat, and there were shouts and piercing whistles mingled with the persistent cries of the bewildered animals as they were herded into one of the holding pens behind the woolshed.

Rachel felt some sympathy for the sheep, but thought it might have been fun up there on the sunbrowned hills, winkling them out from the gullies where the coarse bracken caught at their long fleeces, and from the patches of totara with their tall pinetree tops, and the flimsy shelter of the windswept manuka. The hills looked different without their scattered population of sheep. The grass was coarse and brownish and the sun seemed harsh on it, giving it a metallic look. The spiky-tufted, slender cabbage trees that rose from the slopes cast flimsy shadows and offered no shady havens for sheep or men. Here and there an ancient blackened stump reared, jagged and gaunt, a harsh testimony to the ruthless methods of the nineteenth century, when the bush had been put to the flame to make way for grass and the sheep.

Her foster-mother's voice, sharp with exasperation, recalled her to the kitchen, and she repressed a sudden irritation, a faint rebellion at the decree that riding in the muster was work for men, while their womenfolk laboured to satisfy the appetites that were stimulated by their hard work.

The musterers had to be fed at the end of the day, and as well as the electric stove the old range, black and formidable, that was built into one wall of the kitchen, had been brought back into service. A pile of neatly sawn kanuka logs stood on the hearth, and Anne, arms to the elbows in flour as she kneaded a bowl of dough, wanted Rachel to feed the greedy flames.

'I'm sorry,' said Rachel, opening the metal door with a poker held under the handle, and pushing two pieces of wood on to the lowered flames inside. 'I was watching the muster.'

'Yes, well, there are more important things to watch,' the other woman said, more gently. 'You keep your mind on the job, my girl. Will you grease some trays for me? They're over in that corner by the stove.'

Rachel greased them and helped to put the fat white squares of dough on them as Anne cut them with quick, busy strokes of her old kitchen knife, softly thumping on to the floured board beneath.

The stove was making the big kitchen hot to work in. Auntie Anne's face was flushed, and Rachel wiped the back of her hand over a forehead that was warm and clammy.

'You're looking very like your mother these days,' Auntie Anne said suddenly.

'Am I?' Rachel didn't remember, but a photograph that her father had always had now stood on the pine dressing-table in her room. It was a wedding photo, with her father looking strangely young and with hair unnaturally smooth, and his arm around a girl whose smile looked pensive. She was holding a bouquet of roses and maidenhair fern and her dark eyes, staring at the camera's eye, looked gentle and a trifle apprehensive.

She didn't remember that Auntie Anne had ever mentioned her mother before. 'You mean—from her photo?' she asked. 'You didn't know her, did you?'

'I'm afraid not.' The other woman shook her head. 'Your father told me she died before you came here. Did he tell you much about her?'

'No. He said she was beautiful and sweet-natured, and she didn't deserve to die. It seemed to hurt him to talk about her, so as I got old enough to see that, I didn't ask him to.'

Anne shook her head again, this time in sorrow. 'He never got over her death, it seems to me.'

'He said once that if it hadn't been for me, he would have followed her.'

Anne looked disapproving at that, and Rachel went on, 'Another time, he said it was his fault that she died. He wouldn't explain what he meant.'

'Open the oven.' As Rachel obeyed, the other woman picked up the trays and slid them into the racks, then straightened up and looked thoughtfully at the girl. 'Did your father tell you much about himself?'

'What do you mean?'

'Did he ever tell you what he did before he came here with you?'

'Not—really. I know he'd travelled a bit. He used to talk about England, and Italy, and Greece. We had books about them, you know, and he would tell me what they were really like—how it was to be there.'

'Yes—books.' Anne paused significantly. 'Doesn't it seem strange that a roustabout—an odd-job man, had so many books? He was very well-educated, your father. He never said?' she paused significantly.

'About what?'

'Well—' Anne hesitated, then said, 'I think you're old enough to know. I'm not certain, mind. But I think your father was a doctor.'

'A doctor!'

'That's what I said. You know, he always looked after the sick animals, and there was one time—well, you remember Huka?'

The youngest child of one of the Maori families that had moved away. A bright, brown-skinned little streak of light-

ning, always in trouble, always covered in scratches and
bruises and grubby, frayed bandages, because his ambitions
persistently outstripped his capabilities, and he had never
learned to look before he leaped.

'Yes, I remember him,' Rachel said, with a faint, remini-
scent smile.

'Well, he was born two months too soon. His mother
should have gone into town beforehand, but of course with
such an early labour—and fast, it was too—we had to cope
as best we could. It turned out to be a breech, and I don't
mind telling you I was in a bit of a state, trying to help the
woman, when your father came in and just took over. He
told her what to do, told *me* what to do, and in no time
it was all over. The baby was fine, the mother was well, and
I was enormously relieved, I can tell you.'

Rachel felt disorientated. 'Did you—did you *ask* him
how he knew what to do?' she asked.

'Yes, of course. He muttered some nonsense about common sense and us not being so different from animals. And
then he asked me not to mention it any more. I did tell
Dr James about it, eventually, because I couldn't take the
credit to myself for what your father did. But when he
went over there to see your father, he got very short shrift.
Your father wouldn't discuss it with anyone, and that was
that.'

In her own room later, Rachel mused over the astonishing
disclosure. *Had* her father been a doctor? And if he had,
why had he given up his practice to spend his life as a
farm roustabout? The death of his wife, perhaps, as Auntie
Anne had hinted.

She looked at the wedding photograph. It gave her no
clues and little comfort. It was the only photograph she had
of her father, and he didn't look at all as she remembered
him ... It might have been a stranger wearing a mask that
vaguely resembled his features.

And her mother, palely pretty in her wedding gown. Had
she loved him as much as he loved her? Had his feelings
of guilt about her death had any real foundation, or were

they an outcome of his grief, and illogical belief that he could have saved her, *if* ...?

She would never know, so it was no use worrying herself with speculation about it. Her father had left no dramatic letter to be opened after his death, no diary to unfold his past life to her. All she had were memories, his books and a wedding picture.

The shearers arrived the next day, sweeping into the yard in two noisy, dust-laden vehicles, and humping their gear into their quarters with rough good humour. Some gangs were provided with their own cook, but Anne had always prided herself on her ability to provide for all who came to the station, whether workers or visitors. Two freshly killed hoggets already hung near the back door to provide a variety of chops, roasts and stews, and an enormous pot of soup, thick and tasty, with just-pulled carrots and home-grown onions floating on the top, was steaming gently on the side of the old black stove.

Rachel joined in the preparation with determined energy, earning a rare word of praise from her foster-mother.

'You're a good girl, Rachel. You'll make some man a fine wife one of these days. Your father would be proud of you.'

Rachel grinned, warmed by the complimentary tone, but a little amused at the words. Her father had treated house-work and cooking as something necessary but to be kept to a minimum, and the two of them, when she was old enough, had tackled it together, often talking about other things as their hands were occupied peeling potatoes or cleaning floors. She doubted that her father would have taken a pride in her ability to thicken a stew or steam a pudding big enough for a shearing gang.

To Auntie Anne, housewifery approached the level of art, and while Rachel admired her flair for making a comfortable home and feeding a virtual army when neces-sary without turning a hair, the thought of making her own life's work the running of a homestead filled her with a vague and indefinable depression.

She hadn't seen Damon since her birthday. She had felt a little shy and uncertain over the next few days, concerning him, and then the muster had begun, and once shearing started, Anne kept her fairly busy.

When the shearing was well under way, she took advantage of a spare hour to slip down to the shearing shed and watch. It was always a fascinating spectacle, although she was sorry for the sheep and the smell was inclined to be rather overpowering.

She watched a brawny Maori haul in a rather recalcitrant ewe through the swinging door behind his place on the shearing stage, and expertly wrestle her into a helpless position between his knees, then deftly remove the fleece with long sweeps of the electric shearing blade before allowing his pink and chastened victim to escape into the pen.

The man beside him was younger and not so broad, but his black woollen singlet—the 'uniform' of the shearers—revealed healthy muscles moving under a deeply tanned skin. His hair was fair and wavy and worn quite long. He was working fast and Rachel noticed him giving swift sideways glances at the men on each side of him now and then.

He finished the animal he was working on, and kicked the fleece out of the way, where it was picked up by one of the women shed-hands and taken to the sorting table. The fair young man lost no time in dragging in his next sheep, flipping it expertly to sit between his knees, looking uncomfortable but docile as he relieved it of the thick wool; the fleece falling away as he worked to reveal its clean white inner softness in contrast to the grubby, greyish outer wool.

The man worked with almost feverish swiftness, and Rachel bit her lip as a small nick in the animal's skin began to ooze blood, and then, as he flipped the sheep over, another appeared behind its ear in the wake of the clippers.

He was a good shearer, and obviously wanted to be a fast one, but he was not a top shearer, not if he damaged too many sheep like that too severely. He was pushing his speed too much, at the expense of the sheep, measuring his time against that of the older man beside him, who had probably been shearing a lot longer.

He gave the sheep a push to send it on its way, and briefly stood for a moment, looking straight at Rachel, before he turned to bring in another.

Briefly, but with disconcerting effect. He had very blue, very *bold* eyes, and raked her with a frank male glance that made her cheeks burn and convinced her that he had noticed her before she had begun to watch him. That the performance he was putting on up there was primarily for her benefit.

Uneasily, she turned away and walked over to the sorting table, where two Maori women were deftly pulling apart the fleeces, discarding the dirty and flawed wool and piling the rest into bags for pressing.

Rachel watched for a while, then could not resist looking back at the stage to see how the shearing was going. The fair man was bent over his work, his hair falling across his face, and she thought what a nuisance it must be, and that he must be rather proud of his appearance, to put up with that. He pushed away the sheep and tossed back his hair, his glance swiftly raking round the big shed and finding her. Instead of turning away immediately as last time, he stood, apparently resting, hands on his hips, legs apart, his chest heaving slightly with exertion, and the dark tan on his arms and chest sheened with sweat. His eyes challenged hers, and she felt a stirring of attraction to his young, blatant virility. Slowly he smiled at her, confidently, and she was suddenly ashamed of her reaction and looked away.

A few minutes later she left the shed, carefully not looking at the young shearer, but very conscious of him all the same.

She went swimming that evening, when the sun was almost gone and the sky streaked with a wash of gold that ghosted the waves with its pale reflection.

She slipped past the cottage without pausing to knock on Damon's door, hoping that he would be busy and perhaps not notice her. There were other stretches of coastline to swim, but none as safe or as private as this little beach, and none that would solace her tumultuous and confused thoughts and emotions as the one that she always thought of as a sort of home.

She stayed in the water for nearly an hour, swimming lazily in the waves that were slow and soft with the approach of evening, and when she came out the cool air made her shiver and it was almost dusk.

She dried herself and pulled on jeans and a loose, light sweater and combed her hair. Then she thrust the comb into the pocket of the jeans, and swinging the towel in her hand, climbed the steep path.

Damon was sitting on the step of the cottage, leaning against the door jamb with a book in his hands. Rachel stopped walking when she saw him, because he wasn't reading the book, although it was open. He had obviously been waiting for her to appear.

She knew she should say something, but she was suddenly tonguetied, and when he stood up she experienced an illogical spasm of alarm.

'Good evening, Rachel,' he said.

'Hello.' She stood where she was, and didn't move any further.

'I didn't knock,' she said. 'I thought you might be busy.'

'You don't have to make excuses. If you prefer to swim alone, you're entitled to. Would you like a drink?' He motioned towards the door as though inviting her tacitly to enter.

'I—should be getting back.'

He smiled and said, 'You know, I have the oddest feeling that you don't always do what you should.'

'Oh, but I *do*!' she assured him quickly, adding in all honesty, 'Mostly.'

He laughed and stretched out a hand. 'Come on in for a minute.'

As she hesitated, shifting her feet, he said rather drily, 'I won't pounce on you, you know. The kiss the other night was just a birthday salute—a sort of friendly welcome to the adult world. Not a prelude to rape ... or seduction.'

For some reason that both infuriated and hurt her, and

she said heatedly, 'I didn't think—what makes you think that I—you *beast*!'

'Now, that's definitely an exaggeration,' he said mockingly. 'I might have been a bit premature, but bestial I deny!'

'I—that wasn't what I meant, and you know it!'

'All right! Peace. I promise not to tease you any more if you'll come and relieve my loneliness for ten minutes.'

Disarmed, she asked, 'Are you lonely?'

'Infinitely.'

And although she didn't quite believe him, she went inside with him, then, and took the chair he indicated while he went into the kitchen to fetch the drinks.

He had left his book lying on the table nearby, and she picked it up. It was a book of poems by Hone Tuwhare, a Maori—*No Ordinary Sun*.

When Damon returned and put a glass of orange juice at her elbow she glanced up and then returned to the poem she was reading, and let out a held breath in a small sigh as she reluctantly closed the book and took up her glass.

'Do you like poetry?' Damon asked.

'Oh, yes. I write——' she broke off and buried her nose in the glass, draining half if it in her hurry.

'You *write*?' he repeated, with unmistakable interest. 'Poetry?'

'Well——' she muttered, shrugging, 'I just scribble things down when I feel like it.'

'Poetry sort of things?'

'Well—yes. But just for myself, you know.'

She had started after her father died, and no one knew of it, but she had books full of poems, scribbled in pencil, and other books with her favourite ones, the ones that meant something when she read them again, copied out and sometimes revised, in her neatest printing, done with a fine old Parker pen which her father had always carried with him.

Words had always fascinated her, and she had found in writing her poems a way of using words to distil and capture fleeting pleasures and griefs, and deeper emotions, loneliness and despair and hope. She had even recaptured the happy moments she had shared with her father in brief poems of remembrance.

Damon was looking at her in thoughtful silence, as though he was thinking deeply about something perhaps nothing to do with her. She was relieved when he began speaking about something else altogether.

He asked how the mustering was progressing and she told him they had started shearing today, and that she and her foster-mother were busy cooking for the gangs. She wanted him to know that she had not deliberately stayed away—or, if that was not quite true, at least she wanted to tell him she had a good excuse. She wondered if it was true that he was lonely. He had said he was not such a hermit as the character in his new novel.

They talked, and time flowed by until it was almost dark completely, and he insisted on walking almost all the way back to the homestead with her, although she knew the path even in the dark as a cat knows its chosen pathways night or day, and she told him he was more likely to break an ankle on the way back than she was to come to any harm. But he just laughed and came along anyway. He left her when the lights of the house were close.

She had to skirt the men's quarters where the shearing gang slept to get to the house, and as she rounded a corner of it, a shape detached itself from the shadow of the building, giving her a fright and bringing her to a sudden, heart-thumping stop.

A small, glowing red light moved, and she recognised it was a cigarette, and the shape was a man, early moonlight gleaming on fair hair. She made out the general shape of him in the dim light, and knew it was the young shearer she had been watching that afternoon. The one with the insolent eyes and the knowing smile.

'Hi there,' he drawled. 'You're the sheila that was in the shed today.'

'That's not my name,' she said stiffly, and she heard him laugh.

'What is it, then?' he asked.

'Rachel Standen.'

'Standen,' he repeated thoughtfully. 'Not Langholm. Y're not the boss's daughter, then. You work here?'

'I live here,' she said. 'I have to go in now.' He was blocking her path and she hoped the hint would move him, but it didn't.

'If you're not the daughter,' he asked, 'how come you live here, Rachel?'

'That's not your business,' she said, deciding quite definitely that even if he did have a fine physique and a handsome face, she didn't in the least like this insolent young man.

'So-orry!' he said, with exaggerated contrition. 'Just trying to be friendly, Rachel. My name's Des. Desmond William Alexander.'

He put out a hand in the dimness, and unwillingly she put hers into it. 'Hello, Des,' she said, as his grip tightened a little on her attempt to withdraw from it. 'And goodnight,' she added firmly. 'I really do have to go in.' She pulled on her hand and he reluctantly let go, still standing in front of her.

'See you tomorrow?' he said.

'You probably will,' she said casually, hoping that would satisfy him.

'Coming to the shed?'

'I don't know,' she answered, thinking she would keep away from it in future. 'I'm kept pretty busy at the moment. Goodnight.'

Determined to get away from him, she moved forward, but he just stood there, and she had to veer sideways and walk round him, pushing past a twiggy korokia which caught at her clothes.

'G'night, Rachel,' he said. 'See you tomorrow.'

In the middle of the night she woke from a terrifying dream in which Des Alexander had been dragging her by the hair to the shearing stage, his electric shearing gear in one hand buzzing, then rising to a shrill, throbbing note, as he thrust it under her hair. Horror woke her.

The sound continued after she opened her eyes on the

comforting darkness of her room, and she realised there was a cricket on her windowsill, singing a piercing solo to the background chorus of others of its kind further distant.

Her heart seemed to be keeping pace with the rapid throbbing of the cricket's song, until the lingering fear left by the nightmare ebbed away, and she was able to lie calmly and identify other night sounds that soothed her— the continuous muted booming of the sea, a dog barking intermittently as something disturbed his slumber, the muted owl call of a distant morepork waiting gleam-eyed for some small unwary prey.

The net curtains at her window stirred in a faint night breeze, and the stars seemed to sway in the sky in a faraway dance. She smiled and her mind began to spin a poem, the words floating into her head like small whispered secrets of the night. She closed her eyes, weaving words that lulled her eventually back to sleep, but just before oblivion descended gently on her closed lids, she thought distinctly, *I must show the poem to Damon.*

She didn't go to the shed the next day, and she saw Des Alexander only in the distance. Deliberately she kept in the background at mealtimes and let Anne do the serving for the shearers while she tended matters at the stove.

She didn't see Damon either, and although a memory lingered of a sleepy desire to show him her poem about the stars, she put it down to the half-dreaming state she had been in at the time. She had never let anyone read her poems and although she had written it down when she woke in the morning, she had no intention of showing this one to Damon or anyone else. He would probably find the idea of stars dancing in the sky childish in the extreme, and worse still, humorous.

The next time she went to the cove, Damon half-raised a hand to her through the window in an acknowledging wave, and went on typing. Rachel went down to the sea alone, and swam for a while, but he didn't come, and, smothering a sense of disappointment, she went home again. He was still working and didn't look up again as she passed the cottage.

The novel must be progressing, she thought, respecting his need to carry on working while the words flowed. He would be feeling good about it, and she forgot her own disappointment in being pleased for him.

The manuka blossoms had dried up and died, but the shell Damon had given her for her birthday still remained on her dressing table, alongside the embroidered brush and comb set that the Langholms had given her for her first Christmas with them, and the photograph of her parents on their wedding day.

She had replaced the manuka with a sprig of the sweetly scented jasmine from the front porch. The perfume lingered in the room and the small pink and white flowers spilled on to the polished surface of the dressing table, investing it with a wayward and charming contrast to the regimented setting of the photograph and the hairdressing set which were arranged according to Anne's instructions. Tidy and efficient herself, she had worked hard at eradicating Rachel's careless ways with clothes and personal belongings, and taught her with patient and sometimes exasperated persistence to follow her own maxim of a place for everything and everything in its place.

Rachel was still guilty of frequent lapses, but for gratitude and Auntie Anne's peace of mind she tried to conform to standards which still made scant sense to her.

The natural untidiness of the jasmine was a small and harmless rebellion, after all.

CHAPTER SIX

THE weather continued hot and dry, so the shearing progressed quickly. The days were filled with the noise from the pens—bleating from the sheep and especially from the lambs separated from their mothers, and the barking of the dogs, bullying the poor woolly creatures into place, and the shrill whistles and occasional shouts from the musterers.

Rachel kept away from the shearing shed. She was busy anyway helping Anne supply the endless cups of strong black tea that the shearers consumed, and the hearty scones and cakes that went with them, as well as the substantial meals that were required. She came to hate the old black stove with its fierce heat and its continual need for more fuel. The kitchen seemed one vast oven itself.

Simply to get away from it, she went to watch the dipping when she had a half an hour to spare. The Langholms still used the old trough method, although some of their neighbours had taken to using more sophisticated shower sprays to get rid of lice and other nuisances that infested their sheep.

The dip smelt strongly of disinfectant and the water was a dark blackish-brown, unpleasant colour. Rachel leaned on the railing beside Jerry, who acknowledged her presence with a brief grin. The sheep came down the narrow race and were forced into the foul-looking water, and Jerry leaned over with a long pole to force their heads under and make sure they were thoroughly dipped.

Rachel couldn't help a small shudder and a soft exclamation of sympathetic disgust.

Jerry turned and grinned again. 'You're too soft, Rachel,' he scoffed. 'It doesn't hurt,' he added kindly.

'I know, but the poor things must think you're trying to drown them!'

Jerry shrugged. 'It's better than having the lice suck their blood.'

Rachel shuddered again, making him laugh, and had to agree.

Anyway, now that they had been shorn and dipped, and the lambs tailed and earmarked, the sheep would be driven back to the pasture on the hills and left in peace until the next muster.

Jerry leaned over again with his pole, and Rachel shut her eyes. She turned her back on the dip and leaned against the sun-warm wood of the rails, looking at the high curves of the hills, and the few billowing clouds pushing up behind them into the aching blue of the sky.

'Maybe it'll rain,' she said half-hopefully, and Jerry glanced around briefly and looked critically at the clouds that had caught her attention. 'Nah,' he said positively. 'They're not rain clouds.' He looked back at her and said, 'Are you coming to the dance on Saturday?'

'What dance?'

'In the district hall,' he said, turning away to carry on with his job. 'You know—the pre-Christmas dance.'

'Oh.' She had vaguely heard there was a district dance planned, but had been so busy and tired that it had slipped her mind. It sounded like a nice change from drudgery. 'I'd like to. Are you going?'

Jerry shrugged. 'If you want to go, I'll take you,' he said nonchalantly.

The shearing should be over by then. It might be fun. 'Thank you, Jerry,' she said, meaning it, and she smiled at him.

''tsawright,' he muttered, shrugging, and a faint wave of colour showed under his healthy tan. Head bent, he pushed another sheep under with some force, and Rachel thought that for the sake of the helpless animals she had better remove her presence.

She was surprised and touched, and naturally flattered, by Jerry's growing interest in her. There was not much opportunity to meet young men in her life. The boys at the summer schools she had attended the last two years, organised by the Correspondence School, had seemed just *boys*. She had enjoyed the few dances she had attended before, but had been a little shy of her partners, and none of them had paid her particular attention, except once when one of them had been the worse for drink. He had steered her into a secluded corner when the lights were low and had forced a kiss on her which she found revolting, his beery breath and hot mouth making her feel sick. She had stamped hard on his foot and made him let her go, and then she had fled to the ladies' room at the rear of the hall to wipe her mouth with a water-soaked handkerchief, and regain her composure. If that was what kissing was like, she wanted none of it.

But it had been so different when Damon had kissed her. The kiss itself had been so brief it was over before she had time to analyse it, but there had surely been nothing repulsive about it. And she had liked the feeling of his arms about her, of his body pressed against hers, somehow safe and solid and very satisfying. With Damon she hadn't wanted to run away and scrub the memory of his lips from hers. She would rather have liked to stay longer in his arms, leaning against his gentle strength, feeling his jacket against her cheek and his warm hands spread against her back.

She knew that Jerry would like to kiss her too. Soon, if she encouraged him, he would. Jerry was nice, and certainly not unattractive, but she was a little wary of the consequences if she did encourage him. Of where it might lead ...

On Saturday night she wore a cool sun-frock with narrow tie-straps at the shoulders that looked crisp and fresh and showed off her golden tanned skin beautifully.

Jerry didn't say anything when she appeared ready for the dance, but his eyes showed his appreciation, and his mother smiled at Rachel and told her she looked very nice, and added the usual instructions to Jerry to look after her.

The hall, when they arrived, was decorated with paper

streamers and cardboard Christmas trees, and the bright lightbulbs had been changed for dim, coloured ones in an attempt to create an intimate atmosphere. Dancing had begun already, and almost as soon as they entered Jerry pulled her on to the floor to dance with him.

He kept hold of her hand afterwards as he greeted his friends, and let it go almost reluctantly when one of them asked her for the next dance.

But when that was over she couldn't see Jerry among the growing crowd, and when the music began again and a pair of strong masculine hands grasped her waist and pulled her back to the dance floor, turning her at the same time, she thought at first it was Jerry, and was surprised to look up and find that it was Des Alexander.

Somehow, they were already dancing, and although she faltered a little in the rhythm of the steps, it would have been too pointedly rude to leave him on the floor.

Des was smiling down at her, looking very handsome and virile in a white silk-knit shirt and dark trousers. His fair hair gleamed in the dim light as they passed under one of the coloured bulbs, and she couldn't help responding to the blatant admiration in his eyes.

'Not going to run away again, are you, Rachel?' he asked cheekily.

'I don't know what you mean,' she shrugged. She had never *run away*, but she had taken good care that when she was around Des, there were plenty of other people around too.

'Yeah?' he smiled wickedly at her. 'You're scared of me, aren't you?'

'Don't be silly,' she said coolly. 'Why should I be scared of you?'

'Dunno,' he said. His voice lowered intimately. 'I wouldn't hurt you, you know.'

She didn't know what to answer, so said nothing, and after a few minutes he said, 'You never came back to the shed. I missed you.'

'How could you miss me?' she said. 'You only saw me there once. Anyway, I'd have thought you would be too busy with your job to notice who was watching.'

'I noticed *you*, all right,' he said softly. 'You were watching me.'

'I watched some of the others, too,' she said. 'You're not the only good shearer in the gang.'

He laughed and said, 'So you think I'm good, do you? You wait——' His face changed and took on an eager, younger look. 'One day I'll win the shears, you'll see.'

'The Golden Shears?' In spite of herself she was interested. The prestigious national shearing championship was the aim of many young men, and remembering his skill with his machine, she believed that in a year or two he might have a chance of winning it.

'Sure,' he said confidently. 'I'm good, aren't I?' he challenged her.

For the first time, she smiled at him. 'Yes, you're good,' she agreed. 'But you try to go too fast for your capability.'

With a slightly hostile look, he said, 'Yeah? You only saw me once.'

Almost tempted to laugh, she said, 'I know. And you were showing off. Maybe you're better when there's no one watching. But in competition you'll have an audience.'

'So, tell me what I did wrong, Miss Know-it-all.'

She glanced at his annoyed face and looked away, refusing to answer.

After a few moments he said in softer tones, 'I'm sorry, then. Maybe I'm touchy about my shearing. So I go too fast and I nick the sheep a couple of times. So what?'

'It'll lose you points, that's what.' *Not to mention hurting the poor sheep*, she thought.

'Yeah, I know,' he conceded. 'So I'll slow down a bit for a while, maybe. Come and watch me again, huh?' he added coaxingly. 'Be my audience?'

She smiled and said, 'Maybe.' In this mood he seemed much nicer and more like a coaxing boy than an arrogant young man.

Jerry reclaimed her for the next dance, and she didn't dance with Des again. She saw him from time to time, dancing with other girls who seemed, from the slightly dazzled smiles they gave him, to be quite taken with him.

Jerry drove her home around midnight, and stopped the car by the back door so that she could get out before he took it round to the garage to put it away for the night. She was turning to find the door handle when the pressure of his arm round her shoulder pulled her towards him, and as she automatically turned up her face to look at him, his lips came down firmly on hers.

She stayed quietly in the circle of his arm, not responding, but accepting his kiss, His mouth was warm and pleasant, and he was taking his time, not demanding anything of her but acquiescence.

He let her go and muttered goodnight to her, and with a sudden rush of fondness for him, she leaned over and pressed a quick kiss on his cheek before scrambling out of the car.

As she was getting into bed a little later she heard him coming in the back door and locking it. As he walked past her room on the way to his own, he was softly whistling.

On the day the shearing was in its last stage, Rachel kept her half-promise to Des and went down to watch again.

He glanced up when she walked into the shed, and gave her a brief grin. He was nearly finished with the animal he was working on, and didn't waste any time dispatching it to the pen and dragging in another.

This time, without looking at Rachel, he worked with quite outstanding care, the long, smooth strokes peeling off the fleece flawlessly so that it fell to the boards in one piece and its erstwhile wearer escaped, bleating indignantly but with not a sign of damage to her shaven skin.

It had been fast, but not too fast for perfection, and as the young shearer grinned across at her and gave a thumbs-up signal, she smiled back in congratulation.

She watched a little longer, walking along the floor to take a look at the rest of the gang, too. But she had to admit to herself that Des was, in spite of his youth, among the best. He might one day realise his ambition and win the Golden Shears award.

She turned to go back to the house, and had reached the door of the shed when Des leapt from the stage and came after her.

'Hey!' he said, smiling. 'How did I do?'

'You don't need *me* to tell you,' she said. 'You know you're good.'

'I'll be off tomorrow,' he told her. 'We've finished here.'

'Yes, I know. Where do you go next?'

'Cater's. It's about thirty miles from here.'

'Yes, I know.' She made to turn away. 'Good luck, Des.'

He caught her arm, and she saw some curious looks being cast in their direction by the shed-hands nearby. 'See me tonight, Rachel?'

She tried to pull away unobtrusively. 'You probably will see me,' she shrugged.

His grip tightened. 'You know what I mean,' he said. 'Say goodbye to me properly. Please?'

'I'm not sure I do know what you mean,' she said warily. 'You tell me.'

He looked reproachfully at her and shook his head, then unexpectedly laughed. 'Boy, you are really suspicious, aren't you?' he asked incredulously. 'What do you *think* I mean?' His hand dropped from her arm and he went on in hurt tones. 'You're a nice girl, Rachel. I don't meet many nice girls in my job—moving around all the time from station to station, there's not much time to make friends. So maybe I came on a bit strong for you the first time I spoke to you, because I'm only here a couple of weeks, right? There's no time for beating around the bush, if I want to make friends. I *like* you. When we talked at the dance, I figured you liked me a bit, too. I can't get to know you round here——' he jerked a thumb in the direction of the shearing shed, '—specially when you're always busy handing out cups of tea and dishing up the *kai*. All I'm asking is ten minutes to talk to you, say goodbye without an audience. How about it, Rachel?'

Loneliness always touched her, and his accusation of suspiciousness made her feel guilty in spite of herself. 'All right,' she said. 'Ten minutes. It will have to be after we wash up tonight. About eight?'

He smiled. 'Meet me here, by the woolshed.'

Conscious of the barely concealed curiosity all about them, she nodded quickly and slipped away.

Later she began to feel uneasy about it. She hardly knew Des, and although he had sounded so plausible, the meeting had the flavour of a secret assignation. But her father had taught her never to break a promise, and in spite of her misgivings she left the house soon after eight, telling Anne she was going for a walk. It should have been easy to add that she had promised to meet the young shearer, but she had the feeling that the other woman would ask too many questions and make altogether too much of it, so she went feeling guilty and faintly miserable.

He was waiting for her, leaning against the timber wall of the shed, watching as she walked towards him, and only straightening up when she stopped in front of him.

'Good girl,' he said, reaching for her hand, but she evaded him, saying, 'Let's walk.'

He shrugged, and fell into step alongside her as she strolled along the grass, parallel with one of the post and wire fences that divided the paddocks.

She talked about the shearing, trying to draw him out about his ambitions again. But it was difficult, because he answered briefly, and she soon dwindled into nervous silence.

Des walked close to her, almost crowding her against the fence, and when they reached the corner of the paddock and she made to turn, he put a hand on the corner post and one on the top wire, between the barbs, and imprisoned her.

She said, 'Des——' and put her hand on his arm to push it away, but he only moved it to put it around her and pull her close to him. Her faint protest was stifled against his hot, hungry mouth, and her hand pushing wildly against him had no effect.

Furiously, she kicked out at his ankle, but her shoes were soft and made little impact. He pushed her hard against the fence-post, hurting her back, and when she raised a hand, trying to reach his hair and pull at it, he grabbed her wrist and twisted it behind her.

Managing to free her mouth, she turned her head away from him, saying, '*Don't*! I don't want——'

'Course you do, honey!' he muttered, his quickened breath loud in her ear. 'Why else did you come, eh?'

'I didn't—you said you wanted to talk!' she protested, realising what a fool she had been.

'Talk!' he jeered, and laughed as he pulled at her hair to turn her face back to him. His body was hard against hers, and the wire tied on the fence-post was digging into her back.

'You're hurting!' she protested, but he wasn't listening, and he kissed her again, pushing back her head until her neck ached.

He didn't care that he was hurting her, and she knew he was only interested in his own pleasure, that she might have been any girl at all, a body that happened to be female and available. His mouth on hers was an invasion and an insult, and in desperation she opened her teeth briefly and bit him, a brief, hard nip on his underlip that made him release her in startled fury.

She pushed at him and ducked between his upraised, detaining arm and the fence, feeling one of the barbs on the wire briefly pull at her sleeve as she dived past, intent on escape.

'*You bitch!*' he muttered, as she evaded his grab at her, and sped as fast she could run along the grass towards the homestead.

Fear lent her strength and speed, and although he gave chase briefly, he gave up before she reached the woolshed. But his angry shout pursued her in the clear evening air, and she felt shudderingly sick at the ugly words that he flung at her.

She didn't see Jerry until he caught her arm as she almost ran into him. He pulled her to a stop before him, demanding to know what the *hell* was going on, and as he saw Des coming in their direction, he obviously guessed at some of it, his jaw jutting ominously as his fingers unconsciously tightened on Rachel's arm.

'It's all right, Jerry!' she panted, wanting at all costs to avoid more trouble, but he said forcefully, 'It isn't all right, if that bastard's calling you names!'

Half-hysterically, she begged, 'Oh, Jerry, please—it's nothing!'

'You're bleeding!' he said sharply, his eyes on her arm, and looking down she saw that he was right. The barbed wire had torn a hole in her blouse and must have scratched her arm. There was a small red, spreading patch on the torn sleeve. 'Did he do that?' Jerry demanded furiously.

'No! Of course not,' she assured him anxiously. 'It was an accident. I did it myself, trying to get away——'

Too late, she saw that she was making things worse. 'Look, Jerry, forget it,' she pleaded.

'That'll be the day,' he said grimly. 'Get inside, Rachel.' He pushed her gently aside and began striding purposefully towards the other man who was advancing with a kind of wary cockiness.

'No!' She pulled at his arm. 'Jerry! It was my own fault——'

'What was?' he asked. 'Are you going to tell me just what has been going on?'

'He—he kissed me, that's all. It's nothing, Jerry!'

'Did you want him to?' he asked belligerently.

'No. But——'

'Right, that's all I need to know. Now get inside,' he repeated, shaking off her hand.

Des was standing a few feet away now, his thumbs hooked into his belt, feet apart, obviously spoiling for a fight. Rachel stood helplessly, not knowing how to avoid what was inevitably going to happen.

'Your girl, is she?' Des asked Jerry in almost friendly tones, casting a contemptuous glance at Rachel.

Jerry seemed to stiffen all over, but he hardly hesitated before he said evenly, 'Yeah, that's right.'

'She didn't tell me,' said Des, flicking another glance in her direction. 'Tell you what you've got yourself there, mate—she's a proper little——'

Rachel had never heard the word he used, in spite of her years on the station, but it was very explicit, and she didn't need to have its meaning explained. Even before it was out of the man's sneering mouth, Jerry was launched at him, his fist just missing as Des turned his head and ducked, bringing his own fist smashing into Jerry's ribs.

Tempted to scream, Rachel kept her lips clamped shut, watching in sick horror as the two of them hammered and flailed at each other, and wincing as she heard the thick sound of the blows landing and their involuntary grunts of pain.

She wanted to run and hide her eyes, but in some way she was responsible for this, and watching was a penance and a kind of reparation.

She pressed against the wall of the shed, praying that they would stop, her fingers digging into her cheeks. The combatants were locked in a ghastly parody of an embrace now, then they tripped on a projecting rock in the ground and both fell. She thought that might bring them to their senses, but they rolled about on the dusty grass, still grappling with each other, and punching at each other's faces.

Finally Jerry lurched to his feet, panting noisily, fists poised for more, but Des didn't follow. Rachel lowered her hands from her face, her heart tight with dread, but the man was moving, heaving himself into a sitting position, his forearms on his raised knees, head bent on to them, his bent back heaving with the effort of drawing breath into his bruised body.

He said something which Rachel didn't hear, and Jerry gradually relaxed and stepped back, looking at Rachel as she came away from the deep shadow of the shed. 'I told you to go in,' he said.

Ignoring that, she looked at Des, keeping her distance, but deeply concerned.

'Is he all right?' she asked apprehensively.

'He'll live,' Jerry shrugged. 'Come on.' He took her arm roughly and pulled her towards the house with him.

Looking back, she saw Des stagger to his feet and walk

away, and relief unlocked the tension in her chest.

'That was stupid,' she said shakily as they gained the porch. 'There was no need to fight.'

'What did you expect me to do?' Jerry demanded. 'Let him just keep on calling you names?'

He dropped her arm as they entered the house, and made for the bathroom, wiping at a bleeding nose with his hand.

She couldn't answer him, and when he switched on the bathroom light she gasped at the mess his face was in, streaked with blood and dirt. He made for the basin and began running water into it, and she followed him, firmly locking the door, aghast at what his mother would feel if she saw him.

'Oh, *Jerry!*' she cried in distress. 'I'm sorry! Let me help.'

Cleaned up, he didn't look nearly so bad, she was relieved to see. One or two grazes and bruises still showed, but it was not too obvious how he had acquired them.

'Thanks, Rachel,' he said, looking in the mirror and running a comb through his hair. 'I guess I look quite respectable again, now.'

She supposed she should thank him for being chivalrous enough to fight over her good name. 'I wish you hadn't done it,' she said awkwardly. 'But it was kind of you to—protect me.'

'How did you come to be out there with him?' Jerry asked.

'I was stupid,' she confessed. 'He said he'd like ten minutes to talk to me before he left. I thought he seemed lonely, and I promised to meet him. I honestly thought he just meant to talk.'

'You little idiot,' he said scornfully. 'Did he hurt you?'

She shook her head. 'Not really. He was—not gentle, but he only kissed me.' She hesitated, reading the faint question in his eyes and her cheeks grew hot. 'It wasn't true, what he said. I'm not—I didn't tease. All I did was take him at his word and expect him to just talk, when all the time he had something else in mind.'

Jerry nodded as though he accepted that, then smiled. 'I told him you're my girl,' he said.

'I know.' She didn't know what else to say. She didn't know if she wanted to be Jerry's girl, but she was certainly not anyone else's, and she had a fright tonight. Jerry looked very safe and able to take care of himself and her, and she knew him. He didn't frighten her.

She moved, going to the door, and as she turned the lock he came up behind her and slipped an arm about her waist, pulling her back against him and kissing her cheek. His lips were soft and warm, and he smelt of soap and the disinfectant she had put on his scratched face. The knuckles of the hand on her waist were bruised and on one the skin was broken.

His lips nuzzled at her ear, and in a sudden rush of gratitude and remorse mixed with barely awakened young sensuality, she turned into his arms and put her own arms around his neck, letting him kiss her upturned mouth.

When she pulled away from him she avoided the blatant desire in his eyes and slipped quickly out of the room, making for her own bedroom.

In the morning, Anne took one quick, sharp look at her son's face but said nothing. Rachel heard the shearers leaving, but didn't go out to watch their departure. She had no desire ever to see Des Alexander again.

CHAPTER SEVEN

CHRISTMAS came hard on the heels of the shearing, but preparing the roast lamb with newly picked peas and new potatoes, and stuffing the turkey, seemed child's play compared with the cooking of gargantuan meals for the shearers.

As usual Anne Langholm had made her Christmas cake and puddings in plenty of time, and as usual they were baked and boiled to perfection.

In spite of the heat, traditional fare was still served at the station at Christmastime, and Rachel was only thankful that at least the electric stove could cope and the old black monster in the corner did not add its fierce heat to the kitchen.

For the first time this year none of the Langholms' married children were able to be home for Christmas, but Damon was invited to partake of the ready hospitality of the homestead. He arrived with presents for all of them, and when dinner was over he handed them out.

The men's parcels contained socks and handkerchiefs, and Anne was obviously pleased with her large cut-glass bottle of perfume. Rachel opéned her parcel to find a brand-new volume of the poems she had been reading in his sitting room the night she had let slip that she wrote poetry herself. On the fly-leaf was a simple inscription: *To Rachel, from Damon*, and the date.

She thanked him quietly, and when he was distracted by Bert she curled up her legs beneath her in a corner of the sofa and began to read.

They were original and powerful poems, and she soon became lost in them. When Damon sat down beside her and asked, 'Do you like them?' she looked up with deep dreams in her eyes and said sincerely, 'Oh, yes!'

'I'd like to see some of yours some time,' he said.

But she shied away from that, looking down at the book in her lap and saying vaguely, 'Well—I've never shown them to anybody.'

'Am I "*anybody*"?' he asked softly. 'I thought we were friends.'

'I have several friends,' she said.

For a moment he was silent. Then he said, 'Yes, I'm sure you have. I'm sorry if I've presumed too much on *our* friendship.'

Distressed, she looked up at his suddenly austere face and said, 'No, of course you didn't. I didn't mean to sound rude. It's just that—my poems are very private. Please don't be angry.'

'I'm not angry,' he said, his expression softening a little. 'I haven't any right to be angry with you if you choose not to show me your work. I have to admit that I'm a little disappointed, though.'

She looked at him anxiously, but he was smiling now, and she felt a rush of relief. 'I'm sorry,' she said. 'I'll think about it.'

'Thank you,' he said gravely. Then he turned away to answer some remark of Anne's, and there was no more chance of private conversation.

It was a few days later that she did first let him see a sample of what he called her 'work.' She had come to the bay for a swim and this time when she tapped on the door he had not been at his typewriter, but had come to the door with a sheaf of typescript in his hand that he said he had been revising. 'It's tedious work,' he told her. 'Maybe a swim will clear my head and make it go better afterwards.'

'That sounds like an excuse,' she teased him.

'Of course it is,' he agreed lazily. 'And a damn good one, too. I'll meet you down on the beach.'

Rachel ran down the path smiling, stripped off her jeans and shirt and was in the water when he came down.

The water was glorious and they stayed in a long time, flinging themselves down side by side on the warm sand afterwards to dry off in the sun.

Rachel lay on her back, watching the white floss of the clouds that drifted across her vision, and the dipping and wheeling of the gulls uttering their strange cries across the sea. The pohutukawas were in full bloom along the farther cliffs, the blood-red blossoms overhanging the water where it surged around the rocks at the end of the bay. When the flowers began to fall they would turn the water red and summer would be drawing to a close.

She reached for her jeans and drew out of the pocket the small notebook and stub of pencil that she carried with her. Damon was lying face downwards, and seemed to be sleeping. Rachel sat up and began scribbling down the poem that was filtering into her mind, triggered by the warm red of the pohutukawa, the surging water below, the thought that it would all be gone with the summer, when the blossoms paled and dropped themselves in the relentless, seasonless sea.

She didn't realise that Damon was watching her until she had finished, re-read it and scratched out a word, then written it in again. She dropped her hands, holding the book, between her knees then, and took a deep breath, looking out to sea.

Damon turned over and leaned on his elbow, and when she turned her head to look at him he was regarding her with curiosity.

With an automatic reflex action of secrecy, she covered the notebook in both hands and began to turn away, but he shot out a hand and grasped her wrist, pulling it towards him. It was still open at the page she had been writing on, but he wasn't looking at that, he was looking at her face.

'Have you been writing another poem?' he asked gently.

Rachel, unable to tug away from his hold, gave up and nodded.

'May I read it?'

Resentfully, she said, 'Why ask? You're stronger than I am, anyway.'

To her surprise he seemed angry at that. 'I am asking,' he told her, abruptly releasing her. 'May I?'

Slowly she handed the notebook over to him, and watched as he read what she had scribbled there.

He read it once, then sat upright, shooting a glance at her, and read it through again.

When he had finished he looked at her again, then began riffling through the pages of the book, seeing how much she had written. Involuntarily her hand went out to take it from him, and his fingers stilled on the pages, but he didn't give it back to her. His eyes held hers questioningly —almost demandingly—and she dropped her hand and gave a little nod of permission, turning away to watch the sea and the gulls as he read the rest of the poems.

He seemed to take a long time over it, and when he finally handed back the notebook he didn't say anything, but lay back with his head on his clasped hands while Rachel returned it to her pocket and then began to pull on her clothes over her swim things.

'Don't you want to know what I think of your poems?' he asked.

She glanced down at him briefly. 'It doesn't matter what anyone thinks. I write them for myself.'

'Good for you. That's how a true poet should feel. But haven't you ever thought of being published?'

She laughed incredulously. 'I'm not good enough for that!'

He was looking intently at her. 'Would you like to have an expert opinion on that?'

'Yours?' she asked warily.

'No. I'm not an expert on poetry, but I do think you're talented enough to at least think of publication, I know an editor who might be interested—I know he's looking for original talent for an anthology he's working on. I'd like to send him some of your work, and even if he doesn't use any of it, he could give an opinion on how good it is. Will you let me contact him for you?'

She looked at him, thinking about his suggestion, about some stranger reading her innermost thoughts and feelings as she had scribbled them down in all those cheap little notebooks. And her heart cringed.

'No!' she said vehemently. Then, because he was trying to be kind and helpful, she attempted to soften her tone. 'No, thank you, Damon, I don't think so. I'd better be getting back now.'

She turned to go, but he came to his feet and caught at her arm.

'Rachel——'

Reluctantly, she met his eyes. 'Yes?'

'Don't turn it down, just like that.'

'I *must*!' she said. 'You don't understand.'

'Maybe not. Why don't you explain?'

She bit her lip, looking away from him. 'It would be—if they were published—exposing something private and secret to the world.' She looked back at him, her eyes trying to convey her feelings to him. 'Don't you see? It would be like—undressing in public.'

He smiled, his eyes faintly tender on her face. 'Yes, I do see. I guess novelists have a better disguise than poets, but believe me, I do understand.'

His hold on her arm slackened and slipped to her shoulder, and he turned her to walk up the path.

When they reached the top she turned to face him, his hands warm and hard on her waist, his eyes intent and darker than she had ever seen them.

'Do you know your Bible, Rachel?' he asked. 'You have a biblical name, after all.'

'I've read most of it,' she said.

'Then you'll remember the parable of the talents,' he said.

'Yes—the one about the master who was angry with his servant because he buried the talent he gave him, while the others used theirs to make money.'

'That's right. The Master doesn't approve of people burying their talents. They're supposed to be used for the good of the world.'

She moistened her lips with the tip of her tongue and said, 'You're twisting it.'

'I don't think so. I believe anyone with a talent should use it—that gifts are meant to be shared, not used solely for one's own satisfaction. I believe you may have a special gift, Rachel.'

She shook her head. 'The world won't miss it.'

'How do you know? If you can give one person an insight into life, comfort one person's sorrow, make one person understand what happiness means—have you the right to withhold that?'

'You make me sound selfish.' She frowned, taking in what he had said, scarcely believing it. '*Can* my poems do that?'

'They did it for me,' he said quietly.

She made a soft sound of bewildered surprise, and irrelevantly wondered for what sorrow he had found comfort —the death of his parents, perhaps, that he had once spoken of? 'I'm glad,' she said softly.

'Rachel——' his hands left her waist to frame her face, softly brushing back her hair, and resting lightly on her skin, his thumbs gently stroking her cheeks. 'Trust me——?'

'Yes.' She did trust him, and to prove it she took the notebook from her pocket and gave it to him. He stepped back from her, holding it in his hand and smiling at her. 'I'll bring some more tomorrow,' she promised rashly, now that she had committed herself. She turned to go, suddenly shy, feeling that she had given a part of herself up into his keeping. But he caught her shoulder and brought her round to face him, and his head bent to feather a brief, light kiss across her brow.

'Thank you, darling,' he said.

Endearments seldom came her way, and as she made her way across the rough grass, she recalled that *darling* with warmth and a little confusion. Damon probably called lots of girls darling—he moved in the sort of circles where such words meant very little, but he had sounded as though he meant it. Of course, he had been pleased with her for giving in.

She brought him all her notebooks the following day, going away again immediately with the excuse that she was needed back at the homestead. For the next few days she hovered between embarrassed shyness and tentative expectation when she thought of Damon reading them. One part of her wanted to fly over to the cottage and demand to know what he thought of them while another panicked at the thought of his assessing grey eyes and his sharp intelligence dissecting her naïve outpourings.

Finally her curiosity forced her to return to the cottage and see him. Not wanting to blurt out immediately that she wanted to know his opinion, she said she had come to swim, but it wasn't until afterwards, when she was sitting in the cottage with a glass of orange juice, that he mentioned them.

'I typed out some of your poems and sent them to the editor I spoke of,' he told her.

She looked at him in sudden fright, and he said with a hint of impatience, 'Don't be so nervous. He may not like them, anyway. And then you can crawl back into your shell and hide from the world as you want to.'

Stung by his tone, she said, 'If he doesn't like them, that's only one editor's opinion, anyway, isn't it?'

Obviously surprised, Damon burst out laughing, and said, 'I see. You're not so indifferent to literary fame and fortune, after all.'

Surprised herself, she said, 'I don't know about fame and fortune, but is it possible to make a living from poetry?'

'Probably not,' he said slowly. 'Very few do. But it is possible to make a name. Would you like that?'

'I don't know,' she said. 'It doesn't seem important. But I think I *would* like to see my name in a book. I suppose that's egotistic.'

'I suppose it is,' he agreed rather drily. 'But there's nothing quite like it. Welcome to the club.'

Of course, he knew the feeling. He was smiling at her, and she smiled back, a little apologetically, because she hadn't meant to label him as an egotist. Not that he seemed to mind, too much. She rather liked the idea of being in the same 'club' with Damon.

She got into the habit of spending some time with Damon almost every other day. The weather had turned very hot, and she swam often. Sometimes when the tide was low they would scramble round the rocks at the end of the bay together, and she would point out the sea-life in the rock pools to him, for he had a townsman's ignorance of names of the creatures that inhabited the coast. She showed him where to find the spiny *kina*—sea-urchins, and laughed when he refused her invitation to taste the jelly-like red flesh. She had learned as a child to follow the example of the Maori children, who regarded *kina* as a delicacy fit for kings. She could name most of the shells that were washed up on the beach, from the common oval pipi shells to the rarer volute spiral shells with their cream and brown markings, and the spectacular large trumpets edged with tiger-stripes that they seldom found undamaged.

Damon treated her these days with a sort of friendly indulgence that he might have shown a younger sister he was rather fond of, and her reserve gradually disappeared with him as she grew more confident in his company. Once or twice she caught a look in his eyes compounded of faint exasperation and something else that made her catch her breath and turn away from him, to find something of absorbing interest that she brought to his notice. And next time she looked up, it was to find his eyes back to their normal cool greyness.

But one day she grew bolder and didn't turn away. She had been picking her way round the rocks, and was in the shade of one of the old pohutukawas that clutched at the cliffside with its rough grey roots, the twisted branches, laden with blooms, affording handholds to help her skirt the base of the cliff. She grabbed at one of the branches and it dipped, scattering soft red pohutukawa blooms over her shoulders, bared by a halter-necked top, to drop to the smooth rock under her feet. The cool tickling sensation made her give a soft laugh, and she looked back at Damon who was only a few feet behind her.

She saw the warmth and male appreciation in his eyes as he drew closer, and she didn't move. She still stood there with a hand on the branch and her eyes holding his, when he was only inches away, and when he put his hands on either side of her, making the branch sag further under his touch until it was behind her waist, she met his look without fear.

'Well?' he said softly, confusing her.

'Well, what?' she asked.

He smiled, and his eyes dropped to slowly run over her scanty top and shorts, and then to her throat, and lingered on her mouth. There was faint laughter in them when they returned to hers. Laughter and a certain wary speculation.

'I wonder what you're up to, my little child-witch,' he murmured.

Moving her head a little, she said, 'Don't call me that!'

'Why not? It's what you are. And right now I do believe you think it might be fun to try your enchantments out on me.'

She shook her head in mute denial, not knowing how to answer him, staring at him with hurt in her eyes.

'Don't!' he said, and moved his hand to touch her lips with his finger, lightly tracing the shape of them with an absorbed, almost brooding expression on his face. 'Don't be hurt.' His hand moved to her hair, stroking it back behind her ears. 'I'd love to kiss you, Rachel, but things would never be the same afterwards, you know. I'm not suitable material for your adolescent experiments.'

She flinched at the unexpected cruelty, and she saw his eyes darken and his mouth compress as though it had given him pain to inflict it.

'I don't go in for adolescent experiments,' she said with dignity, as he moved and stood away from her. 'I think your novelist's imagination is running away with you.'

'Do you?' he asked equably, with a hint of laughter. 'Perhaps you're right.'

He was patently indulging her, treating her like a slightly

naughty child who needed humouring, and it made her want to scream and scratch at him. But that would only have proved that she was the child he still thought her; she managed instead to cultivate a cool, adult manner that she hoped would baffle him. He hardly seemed to notice, slipping back easily, it seemed, into his big-brother role for the rest of the afternoon.

When she went home she felt restless and frustrated, and when Jerry asked her with a meaningful light in his eyes after their dinner if she would like to come with him to check on some stock in one of the nearby paddocks, she accepted readily.

She didn't object when he held her hand as they walked, and when on the way back he pulled her into the shadow of one of the looming macrocarpas she met his kiss willingly, and even kissed him back.

He had kissed her several times lately, but this was the first time he had evoked a response, and she was moved by his obvious delight. He kept his arm about her waist as they returned to the homestead, only self-consciously dropping it when his father appeared at the back door of the house.

Summer was speeding to a close. There were days of rain, storms that threatened the summer skies, rolling thunder around the darkened hills. The pohutukawas still bloomed, but their flowers were fading to a dusky crimson and the sea was taking more of them each day.

Damon told her that the editor had liked her poems, and wanted to see more. She gave him permission to send the rest of her notebooks and made herself wait patiently for the verdict on them. With Damon's encouragement and advice, she sent a couple off to a national literary magazine, hoping that they would buy them, accepting his warning that there would be very little money in it, and his teasing smile at her changed attitude to having her name in print. It still frightened her a little, but thrilled her too.

She came to him one day when the sea was sullenly grey, with intermittent showers sweeping curtains of rain across the beach, misty and not cold but depressing.

She hesitated at the door because she could see through the window that he was working, but as she made to turn away he opened the door and drew her in.

She was wearing a summer frock and sandals, with a light cotton jacket thrown over her shoulders which she discarded on his couch. Her hair was sprinkled with raindrops and she impatiently brushed a trickle of rain from her forehead as she sat down.

'What's the matter?' he asked, standing in front of her. Rachel wondered how he knew that something was, but it didn't surprise her, really. Damon knew a lot about her, one way or the other, and she sometimes dreaded his going because then there would be no one who really knew or understood her, at all.

'I just wanted to get out of the house,' she hedged, in answer to his question.

'Any particular reason?'

'I just had to get *away*, that's all!' she said, with a vehemence that surprised herself.

He abruptly turned from her and stared out of the window at the uninviting sea. 'Is it that bad?' he asked.

'Oh—no. Not really.'

'Have you had a row with someone?'

'No. No, nothing like that,' she said. 'But somehow, I —oh, I don't know what's the matter with me.'

'The Germans call it *sturm und drang*, I think,' he said, turning to face her. He looked very mature and sophisticated and rather amused. 'The storm and stress of adolescence.'

'*Why* do you always harp so on my age?' she demanded. 'Eighteen isn't adolescent. I can vote now, you know!'

'You are spoiling for a fight, aren't you? And you *are* still a teenager.'

She swallowed on her anger and said humbly, '*Do* I act like an adolescent?' Perhaps she *was* young for her age, certainly she had little experience of the world outside a few hundred square miles of Hawkes Bay.

'Very rarely,' he admitted. 'Perhaps that's why I have

to keep reminding myself that you are.'

She was on the brink of asking why he had to, but his cool gaze intimidated her. Deep down she knew very well what he meant, even though at the moment there was not a vestige of awareness of her sex in his eyes or manner.

Perhaps in this detached mood he might be able to advise her on her major problem. There was no one else who could possibly help.

'Could I—ask you something?' she asked.

'Ask away.'

'I wouldn't, but there isn't anyone else, you see. Do you know much about—love?'

His eyes suddenly intent, he smiled a little. 'I have some experience of the emotion,' he said. 'In what context were you thinking of it?'

'Well—Jerry.'

'Jerry,' he repeated thoughtfully. 'You're in love with Jerry?'

'That's just the problem,' she said. 'I don't really know. Sometimes I think I'm falling in love with him. He's been quite—I think he's courting me, if people still use that old-fashioned word. Uncle Bert and Auntie Anne seem to approve, and if we love each other, I suppose there's no problem ...'

'But you're beginning to feel trapped.'

She looked up at him, wondering again how he knew her so well.

'You see, I thought that before I married, I'd like to see a bit more of the world,' she said. 'Perhaps go to university, maybe even have a career. Auntie Anne doesn't approve of career women, but I don't think my father would have minded.'

'These days a woman can do both,' Damon pointed out.

'Yes, but I don't really have a particular job in mind, you know,' she said. 'Maybe I should be happy to settle down and get married.'

'*And dwindle into a wife.*'

'What?' she said, smiling uncertainly.

'It's a quotation. From William Congreve.'

'Oh. It sounds rather depressing, doesn't it?'

'Congreve was a cynic. Does the idea of being a wife depress you?'

'No. It never has. I always assumed I'd get married some day, like most people.'

'But not yet?'

'Well—Jerry is older than I am. Naturally he won't want to wait too long.'

'Naturally.' Damon's tone sounded slightly mocking, and she looked sharply at him, but his face was impassive. 'I take it you intend to be a virgin bride?'

Her cheeks flamed with colour but she said steadily, 'I don't see what that has to do with it.'

'Don't be silly,' he said crushingly. 'Is Jerry the only man who's kissed you? I take it he *has* kissed you?'

'Of course he has,' she said. 'And no, he's not the only one. *You* did, for one.'

'My dear girl, if you call that chaste salute a kiss, you've got a lot to learn.'

'Maybe I don't want to learn it,' she said. 'The other men who kissed me—I hated it. It's different with Jerry.'

'How many other men?'

'Two. One of them was drunk. I suppose that hardly counts.'

'Hardly. That's not much of a basis for comparison, is it?'

She looked at him helplessly, and he made an exasperated sound and crossed the room to pull her to her feet, a little less than gently. 'You little fool,' he snapped. 'You *think* you're in love with Jerry—because he rouses your normal sexual impulses, and he's the first man to take the trouble to do so. The two of you have nothing in common but that you're both young and healthy and living in the same house. Does he know anything of what goes on in your mind and heart? Does he care?'

His hands on her shoulders were hard as he told her, and resentfully she said, 'He does care about me! It isn't just sex——'

'I know,' he said more gently. 'But without that you wouldn't even contemplate living the rest of your life with *Jerry*! It's nothing to be ashamed of, but don't be fooled by it either, Rachel. Sexual need can exist without love. What you need is a basis for comparison.'

She went quite rigid as his hands moved from her shoulders and tipped up her head. She was suddenly frightened and he knew it. He barely touched her lips with his warm mouth, and one hand slid down her back to her waist, drawing her up against him, while the other caressed her nape. 'Relax,' he whispered against her mouth. 'Trust me.'

Gradually she did, under his caressing hands, and the featherlight touch on her mouth became firmer. His arms held her closely to him until her head was bent back into the curve of his shoulder as his mouth moved sensuously on hers, until she was drowning in sensation. When his mouth began to draw away, she put up her hands blindly to keep him with her, and as her pleading eyes half-opened she saw his light gaze glittering brilliantly as he smiled down at her, barely a hairsbreadth from her softened lips.

'Open your mouth, darling,' he murmured as he bent to claim it again and she obeyed, instinctively responsive to the increased passion of his kiss.

She felt him draw her down to the sofa until he was sitting on it with her still in his arms, lying across his lap. He kissed her again, deeply and long, his hand shaping her soft breast as she lay against him, trembling with awakened desire.

His mouth left hers and wandered to her cheek and the small indentation beneath her ear. She heard his voice, low and soft, and it was a few moments before the sense of his words penetrated the haze of sensual longing that possessed her.

'Who are you in love with now, my little witch?'

The warmth of his lovemaking suddenly ebbed away as she remembered why he was doing this. A basis for comparison, he had said—proof that almost any man could make her love him by 'rousing her normal sexual impulses.'

She stiffened in his arms, and thrust herself away from him, straightening herself up on the edge of the divan, trying to breathe evenly, but unable to bring herself to look him in the face.

He had certainly made his point, she realised bitterly. Jerry had never made her feel like this. She doubted if he ever could.

CHAPTER EIGHT

'Look at me,' Damon said quietly.

When she didn't move, he put out a hand and lifted her chin, his silvery eyes sharp as he took in the fierce animosity in hers.

'Don't look so murderous, Rachel,' he said mockingly. 'You should be thanking me.'

'For what?' she asked bitterly.

'For a lesson in loving.'

'Loving?' she said scornfully. 'Why don't you call it by its proper name?'

His mouth tightened and he released her abruptly and stood up. Hurt fury drove her on, flinging words at him. 'It was a lesson in—lust, wasn't it? Sexual need that exists without love, you said. Well, thank you for making me feel cheap and dirty with your—*demonstration*!'

He swung round on her then, and she stood up, not wanting him standing over her.

'I told you,' he said, 'it's nothing to be ashamed of.'

'I can't help it! That's the way you make me feel.'

'Oh—*God*!' he exclaimed. 'What a bloody *fool* I am. I should have known better than to kiss a child——'

'I'm not a child and you know it!' she cried furiously. 'You're always going on about how young I am—and we both know why!'

'Yes, we do,' he said quietly, and the glitter in his eyes was a clear warning light. 'That's the first time you've admitted that you know, however. Maybe you *are* growing up.'

'If I am, I'll do it without your help,' she said, breathlessly. She felt as though she had been running, and her body was tense, aware of the tension in him, the tight control he was exercising over his temper.

'Let me know when the process is complete,' he said. 'On tonight's performance, you'll be a knockout.'

Her clenched hand moved sharply and he said, 'Don't hit me, Rachel. I can't guarantee I won't retaliate.'

He looked fully capable of it, his face taut with cold anger and his eyes hard and cruel.

'I'm going home,' she said, trying to stop her voice from trembling.

'Please do,' his curt nod towards the door dismissing her.

Her legs felt weak and rubbery with reaction and she clamped her teeth tightly as she passed him, but it didn't stop the ache in her throat.

'You've forgotten your jacket,' he said as she fumbled with the door handle. He picked it up and as she paused in the open doorway he walked to her and dropped the creased garment around her shoulders. He pulled the collar together and held her there for a long moment. Through the fabric she could feel the hardness of his knuckles against her throat, and she wanted to drop her head on the broad chest in front of her and sob her eyes out. She could see the pulse beat at the base of his throat, the tautness of his jaw and the slightly softened line of his mouth, but she didn't raise her eyes to his.

She said, 'Thank you,' tightly and swallowed back the threatened tears. She was determined to be adult about this if it killed her. Damon was not going to get another chance to jibe at her for childishness.

She walked steadily into the softness of the misty rain without looking back, and she had gone quite a long way before she allowed the tears to mingle with the raindrops on her face. She had an aching sense of loss, as though something precious had been shattered. Damon had said that if he kissed her things would never be the same again. She knew now that he had been right.

But it might have been different if he had kissed her with love. That was what hurt, that he had deliberately and coldbloodedly made love to her to prove a point. He had taken her completely out of her depth and then cruelly

brought her back to reality with that mocking question—
'*who are you in love with now?*'

The rain set in in earnest during the night, creating a
thunder on the iron roof of the house and gurgling in the
downpipes at the corners. It fell steadily all the next day
and the two women were confined to the house except for
brief forays to feed the hens and turkeys, conducted in
oilskins and rubber boots. The men spent the day moving
stock and rescuing young sheep from suddenly swollen
streams and puggy flats, and they came in soaked in the
evening.

The house was dim and depressing and matched Rachel's
mood.

The following day the rain had disappeared and except
for a faint hint of damp cleanliness about the trees it
might never have been. Something was wrong with the
tractor and when it wouldn't start in the morning, Bert
fiddled for a while and with many soft curses located the
trouble, which didn't help much. A new part was called
for, and Jerry was detailed to drive the truck into town
and fetch it.

He asked Rachel if she would like to come along for the
ride, and his mother, having noticed her low spirits, gave
her blessing to the idea. Rachel, glad of the opportunity to
get away from the property for a short time, changed into
a light blouse and denim skirt and climbed into the hard
leather seat of the truck beside Jerry, holding a hastily
compiled shopping list from his mother. It was not a long
one, for Bert would not wait too long for the vital part of
the tractor, but in Anne's opinion an expedition to town
was not to be wasted on only one errand. Rachel could shop
while Jerry tracked down his father's requirements.

They didn't talk a great deal on the way. The road was
tricky after rain, with small slides of rock and muddy clay
sometimes encroaching on to it from the bank, and water-
filled potholes to be avoided as well. Jerry concentrated on
his driving, and Rachel absently watched the bush as
they passed by, the punga fronds dripping on to the truck's

high roof as they passed, and trickles of water ran down between the red ladder-ferns in small waterfalls to the ditch beside the road.

After the long trip, it took only an hour to complete their shopping before they were on their way home again. Rachel had never made such a short visit to town in her life. They had bought some sandwiches and canned drinks which they ate in the truck, and she carefully stowed the empty cans into the used paper bag and placed them in a corner by her feet. Jerry was whistling, and once or twice turned to grin at her between tunes. She smiled back because he was nice and she liked him, and it wasn't his fault that she felt weepy and unhappy.

It wasn't his fault that he didn't know what was in her mind and heart either. He was an uncomplicated person who would be a considerate and kind husband some day, and as long as his wife seemed reasonably cheerful and kept him fed and comfortable, he wouldn't be probing too deeply into her feelings, but would take it for granted that she loved him and was happy. It would be a safe and comfortable existence.

Rachel wished that she could view it with more enthusiasm. She didn't want Jerry to be hurt, and she knew very well that since he had fought and beaten Des Alexander, some male instinct or deeply ingrained conditioning had been at work. A girl he had fought for automatically became 'his girl.' Perhaps she should have disputed it when he had called her that to Des, but a denial at that moment would certainly have been adding fuel to the fire, nothing less than an invitation to both of them to revert to primitive male combat with herself as the prize to the victor.

Keeping quiet hadn't stopped them fighting, anyway, but at least she had not been stupid enough to encourage them in that way. Perhaps afterwards she should have cleared the matter up with Jerry, but in fact she had not really minded at first. Only when Anne and Bert began casting knowing glances and dropping hints that seemed to take it for granted she would be with them as a daughter-in-law one day did she begin to feel uneasy.

She felt a web of kind fondness on all their parts binding her with subtle threads, and not knowing what to do about it, she had been driven to confide in Damon.

His method of dealing with her doubts had been drastic and little short of disastrous. And it hadn't really helped. One part of her acknowledged that he had been right in saying she and Jerry had very little in common, no ground in which their minds and hearts might meet, but she shrank equally from his blunt suggestion that their relationship was entirely sexual, and the sexual dominance that he had himself established so easily over her. Jerry's less practised passion was far more comfortable, if less intoxicating than Damon's dangerous expertise.

When Jerry stopped the truck outside the garage she gathered up the parcels and struggled out, crossing the rough concrete of the yard to the back door as Jerry moved the truck away.

The back door was shut, and she manoeuvred the handle awkwardly, her hands full, then backed into it to open it wide, and turned to kick it shut. The two keys tied on a loop of string that hung on the nail behind the door jingled together as it banged to, and at first the sound meant nothing. She half-turned, then looked again at the keys, still swinging a little on the nail, and her heart began to beat hard and almost painfully.

The slight movement of the keys stopped, and she wrenched herself away from the door and deposited her burden on the bench by the sink. Those keys had always hung there, as familiar as the row of gumboots on the porch outside, as the framed 'Home, Sweet Home' tapestry that adorned the wall. But they had not hung there lately, not for the last three—no, nearly four—months. Not since Damon had rented the cottage.

She knew what had happened even before Anne came into the kitchen and saying, 'Oh, there you are, dear! You were quick. Uncle Bert will be pleased,' began to unpack the shopping.

Automatically Rachel moved to help, her throat locked

tight on the question that shouted in her mind. A spreading numbness seemed to envelop her as she put away jars of food in cupboards and carried a pack of soap to the bathroom.

It wasn't until Anne was carefully re-creasing and folding one of the big grocery bags that she said casually, 'Oh, by the way, Mr Curtis is gone. He dropped the keys in while you and Jerry were away. He said to give you both his regards, and say he was sorry he missed you.'

No personal message for her. Just his 'regards' for both of them. Had he intended to be cruel? Probably not, she supposed. He no doubt often made temporary friends and left them with a casual word to pick up the threads of his permanent relationships again. He would have had no conception of what his friendship had meant to her. Their perspectives were different.

'We didn't see him on the road,' she said.

'He couldn't have been far behind you. He must have gone through the town while you were shopping.'

'Yes, I suppose so. I didn't know he was leaving so soon.' He'd said nothing about it, though she knew his book was nearing completion. He had never been very revealing about it, but she had often enquired about his progress and he had told her he expected to finish 'soon.' That had been vague enough to allow her to push it to the back of her mind and go on living in her fragile fool's paradise.

Anne said, 'He told me he'd completed what he had hoped to do here more quickly than he expected, and now he would like to get back to Auckland to polish it off.' She laughed. 'I expect he's had enough of backblocks life, and can't wait to get back to the city.'

Mechanically, Rachel smiled. Anne was probably right, and not long ago Rachel would have despised him for reliance on 'civilisation' and the trappings of the city. But in the past few months she seemed to have grown up a lot. Her young resentments and prejudices now seemed immensely juvenile. She admitted now her own desire to taste city life, and didn't blame Damon for preferring it.

She went into her room and saw the shell that he had

given her sitting empty on the dressing table. Putting it to her ear as her father had taught her when she was small, she heard the rushing of the sea-sound before she put it down again. She remembered lying on the beach with Damon with that sound in the background, and the gulls crying overhead, the manuka at the top of the cliff bending its white flowers before the breeze, and the gannets circling and diving further out to sea. The sound of the waves had accompanied his first reading of one of her poems—the poem that had been inspired by the waves and the wind and the pohutukawas blooming on the cliff.

Sudden realisation hit her, and the numb shock of his departure was replaced by frantic fear. It held her paralysed for an instant, then she wrenched open her bedroom door and went pounding down the passageway to the back door, pausing only momentarily as she grabbed at the keys, to tell Anne where she was going, not waiting for any objections to be voiced.

She ran all the way, arriving at the little house panting and holding hard to a stitch in her side. She fumbled the key into the lock and flung the door wide, on the neat, bare room, with its small table empty now of all the controlled clutter it had held when Damon lived here.

It didn't take long to search the little cottage, open the drawers and cupboards and confirm what she knew already, deep down.

He had taken her notebooks with him! all her poems were gone.

She wondered what he intended to do with them. Then remembering how angry he had been last time they met, how abruptly he had left, she panicked again and flew out the door to investigate the small incinerator behind the house, and the rubbish bin that stood at the back door.

Slowly, faintly reassured, she returned to the living room and sat down on the sofa.

He would take them to his editor friend, of course, she told herself. Wasn't that why he had asked for them, after all?

He would see that she got them back, wouldn't he?

Or perhaps he would put them in a drawer and forget about them—forget about *her*, a little girl he had once met, and grown quite fond of, even kissed once or twice; a girl who had a little talent that he had carelessly encouraged, but perhaps the talent would look even smaller when he was back among people who took talent for granted, and his enthusiasm would wane. Perhaps the editor to whom he had sent those first poems had not replied because he was embarrassed to tell his friend how bad he thought them.

Or perhaps she was being foolish and should trust him. But he might have left some message for her, she thought with stirring anger. She thought of him sitting on this sofa with her lying in his arms, his voice saying, '*Trust me*,' and later, '*Who are you in love with now?*' And suddenly she was shaking with an anguished fury. She twisted on the seat and thumped her fists against the cushions in a futility of rage, her forehead resting on the worn covering while hot tears darkened the material. 'I hate you, Damon Curtis!' she sobbed. 'I *hate* you!'

When she was calmer, she realised that very likely he had left his address with Anne, and she had only to ask for it and write to him to find out what he meant to do with her notebooks. But she kept putting it off, shy of contacting him, despairing of being able to compose a coolly friendly letter that contained a casual request to know the fate of her poems.

Searching for shelter from emotional storms, she heeded Anne's hints over the years that she was too volatile for her own good, and tried to damp down her emotions and channel them all into loving Jerry. He was lovable enough, she told herself repeatedly, and her warm acceptance of his increasingly frequent embraces delighted him. Anne unobtrusively chaperoned and beamed unmistakable good-will at them, and life was on the surface very tranquil.

One day Rachel received a letter containing a small slip of paper with the information that the editor of the magazine she had sent two of her poems to had accepted them both. It seemed unreal, and she didn't mention to the others what was in the letter, in spite of their curious glances. She was still wondering how to get hold of a copy of the magazine some weeks later, when a rolled copy arrived unheralded in the post.

There was a slip of paper protruding slightly from inside the magazine, and when she opened it at that page she found her two poems printed side by side, and on the paper two scrawled words: *'Congratulations—Damon.'*

'What is it?' Anne asked curiously, watching her flushed face.

Rachel handed over the magazine, retaining the slip of paper in her hand. 'I've had some poems printed,' she said, marvelling at how calm her voice sounded. The warm bubble of excitement that had filled her when she saw her printed name began to fade as she carefully folded Damon's casual note.

'Really, dear?' Anne glanced at the page, noting the name at the foot of the poems and handed the magazine back. 'That's clever of you. I must read them later, when I have time.'

The bubble was extinguished, and later when Anne told the two men after reading the poems and pronouncing them 'very nice,' it was even worse. They were impressed, but puzzled. Bert congratulated her with a rough squeeze of her shoulders, confessing he had never heard of the magazine, and supposed it was 'one of those little jobs.' And Jerry read the poems with an embarrassed air as though he thought it slightly unmanly to do so, and asked her if she got paid for them.

'Not yet,' she said. 'It won't be more than a few dollars.'

'Oh, yeah,' he said, seeming relieved. 'That's good.'

Slightly amused, Rachel wondered if he meant it was good that the pay was trifling, or that she got paid at all, but didn't press him.

Later, in her room, she smoothed out Damon's note and stared at the strong, terse scrawl. It was odd how strongly it brought him to her mind. She remembered clearly the exact line of his mouth, the cut of his hair, the variable shades of his eyes in different moods.

He had not quite forgotten her. It had been kind of him to remember that she might not find it easy to get hold of her own work in print, and go to the trouble of sending it to her. She tried to look at it that way, but as she looked at the brief signature, the bitterness welled up in her, and biting her lip on a sob, she tore the note across and screwed it up before throwing it away.

She had two new poems, and on impulse one day she sent them off with the rural mail to one of the other addresses which Damon had given her. They were returned promptly with a printed rejection slip, and she looked at them with new eyes, decided they were puerile and clumsy, and threw them away. The next time she tried to write the words would not flow, and she felt the frustration of creating something much less than satisfactory, a stumbling and crude version of what her imagination had conceived. It happened again and again, and in a fury of disgust she made a decision to give up writing poetry altogether. It was a childish pastime anyway, and her small success had been a mere fluke.

The weather was turning cold and wintry, and the winds blustered in from the sea, rattling loose windows and stripping the last blooms from the manuka, when she received a long white envelope in the post that contained a stunning surpise.

The editor to whom Damon had first sent her poems informed her that he would like to include one of them in the anthology he was compiling, and after discussion with Mr Damon Curtis, who had shown him some further work of hers, he was interested in compiling a book of her poems for publication on their own.

At first Rachel didn't believe it. But it was there to be read again, and again, and it was true. But why had Damon not told her? She had heard nothing from him but that short note since he left. What did 'discussion' imply? How long ago, and how many times had he discussed her poems with this man—she glanced again at the signature—Carl Watkins?

The hurt that had been dormant began to surface. With a faint hope that Damon might contact her now, she waited a few days, but there was nothing. She read the letter again, then sat down and wrote a carefully worded reply, and deliberately shut the matter out of her mind.

April and May were cold. The cattle had been brought down from the hills and for days the bellowing of separated calves and cows had echoed round the yards, but the final truckload for sale had gone now and the run cattle had been driven back up the lower slopes, while the remaining calves settled contentedly in their winter paddock.

Rain set in for weeks and the wet weather sent the men scouring the hillsides to check for washouts and damaged fences, and endangered stock.

By the time the rain stopped for a week, it was almost June. With fencing needed and other jobs postponed while the rain prevailed, Bert was shorthanded, and Rachel was able to escape the house sometimes with good excuse when it was felt she could help outdoors.

She had been driving the tractor, helping Jerry feed out hay to the stock one day, and doffed her rubber boots and warm jacket on the porch, passing her fingers through wind-tangled hair. There was a car parked in the yard that jolted her for a moment, for although covered with orange-brown mud it was the same make as Damon's, and red too. Rachel wondered who the visitor was, and pulling down her shabby woollen jersey over her jeans, she walked into the kitchen.

Anne and the visitor were sitting at the kitchen table drinking tea, and even as she took a deep, unbelieving breath, the man turned and stood, and she raised her startled eyes to Damon's cool grey stare.

'Hello, Rachel,' he said politely, but she had a distinct impression that his cold manner masked anger with her, and wondered why.

'Hello,' she said, standing uncertainly where she was.

'Come and sit down, dear,' said Anne. 'Mr Curtis has been waiting for you.' Her manner was slightly puzzled.

'I'll go and change first,' Rachel said quickly. 'I'm filthy.'

It had never mattered for afternoon tea in the kitchen, but she had bits of hay in her hair and clinging to her jersey, and the legs of her jeans were splashed with mud.

She wanted to get away from Damon's appraising eyes, and yet when she reached her own room she stripped with frantic haste, leaving her clothes on the mat by the bed in defiance of all Anne's strictures, and hastily donning a fine wool top that skimmed her rounded young figure, and a pair of new dark blue corded slacks. She brushed the fine straws out of her hair and let it fall around her shoulders in soft waves, and smeared a quick dash of lipstick on her mouth.

When she returned to the kitchen, Anne was telling Damon about the rains and the problem of getting farm-workers who would stay, and Rachel sat down quietly and poured herself a cup of tea without interrupting.

Damon looked up and nodded to her without smiling, and then returned his apparently interested gaze to Anne.

They were just finishing their cups of tea when Jerry and Bert came in, and Rachel got up to make a fresh pot, listening as she worked to Damon's explanation that he had been in the district and decided to look them up. Anne had said he was waiting for Rachel, but perhaps that was because he had made a polite query as to her whereabouts and Anne had told him she was expected in soon.

He had been asked to stay the night, evidently, and Rachel was not at all sure how she felt about that. She did know that she was tinglingly aware of his presence, that she felt suddenly more alive than she had for months. There was something about Damon that had that effect on her, like a hand tautening the strings of a violin, bringing them to perfect pitch.

CHAPTER NINE

WHEN the men made a move to return to their work, Damon stood up too, saying 'I'm not a farmer, but if I can earn my keep by helping out in some way for a couple of hours ... ?'

Jerry cast a derisive eye over Damon's well-cut suit and expensive-looking shirt and tie and gave a short laugh. But Bert, giving his son a quelling look, thanked Damon politely and offered to lend him some 'clobber' if he would like to help mend a fence.

When they came in much later, Damon's hair was ruffled, and he had a long red scratch on one hand, while the arms below the rolled-up sleeves of his borrowed plaid shirt were muddy, but he looked less coldly grim than before, as though he had been enjoying himself. He and Bert seemed to have established an amicable relationship, but Jerry was very silent.

When they went into the lounge after the meal that Anne and Rachel had prepared, Rachel sat near Jerry, pulling the hassock from the corner to place it by his chair, ignoring Damon's suddenly narrowed gaze.

After about ten minutes of desultory conversation, Jerry got up and turned on the TV, and Damon rose to slant a challenging glance down at Rachel, saying to Bert, 'Do you mind if I take Rachel out for a walk, Bert?'

Looking faintly surprised, Bert said, 'Of course not, Damon.'

Anne looked sharply from Damon to Rachel, and said, 'It's cool, Rachel. Put your jacket on.'

Damon held out a hand to Rachel to help her up, and his mouth was smiling but his eyes were light and wary.

She took his hand and stood up, and Jerry said loudly, 'I'm coming too.'

Damon looked at him, still holding Rachel's hand in a strong grasp, and said with cool confidence, 'I'm sorry, Jerry, I want to speak to her alone.'

'Why?' Jerry looked belligerent, and his parents uncomfortable.

With deliberate quiet, Damon said, 'We have private business to discuss. If Rachel wants to tell you about it afterwards, that's her prerogative.'

His father said, 'Jerry——' but he ignored it.

'Rachel's *my* girl,' he said.

'Is she, indeed?' Damon murmured, and his fingers on hers tightened painfully. He turned his head to flick an impersonal glance at her flushed face. 'You're engaged?' he asked politely as he dropped her hand suddenly.

'Not yet,' said Jerry. 'But we will be soon. She's going to marry me.'

He looked at Rachel as he spoke, and she saw the pleading in his eyes for her to say yes, to tell Damon it was true. Jerry had rushed headlong into this, and his pride was at stake.

She opened her mouth and said, 'No, I'm not, Jerry. I'm sorry.'

His face suffused with colour, and he swallowed, his mouth opening and then closing in a straight line. Shocked and distressed, she half-moved towards him, and then Damon caught her arm in a painful grip and swung her round towards the door. 'Come on, Rachel,' he said grimly. 'We'll go for that walk.'

Weeping inside, she went with him, standing on the porch while he took her jacket from its hook and pulled it round her, not realising that she should have changed her shoes until they were already wet from the rain-soaked ground. Jerry hadn't deserved that humiliation, although he had asked for it. She had given him every reason to think that she would marry him one day, and it was only when he had come to the point so suddenly and so publicly that she had been hit with the terrible realisation of what she had been heading for. It had not been possible after all to say yes in spite of all the sensible reasons why she should.

Damon had been right to drag her away. The last thing Jerry needed now was her sympathy, especially in front of witnesses.

They were walking towards the sea, Damon in tight-lipped silence, and Rachel desperately blinking away tears of remorse.

She stopped to put on her jacket properly, and he helped her with an impatient touch and then strode on, not touching her.

When they reached the top of the cliff where they could look down at the breakers curling and spraying over the rocks of the headland, he turned and saw the tears in her eyes, shimmering in the dusky light.

Almost roughly he asked, 'Are the tears for Jerry?'

Rachel nodded. 'It was a terrible thing to do to him.'

'Yes.' He turned away, and the tears overflowed and ran down her cheeks. She put up a hand and wiped them away.

Still watching the sea, he said, 'Had you told him you would marry him?'

'No.'

He turned his head then and looked at her. 'Then why did he think that you would?'

'I—suppose—' she whispered, '—because I let him think so.'

'You mean you let him make love to you, but didn't intend to marry him.' Damon said flatly.

'*No!* I *did* intend to—I thought if he asked me I would say yes. It's just—when he sprang it on me like that, I couldn't—'

'I see. My—advice—to you didn't make any difference, then. If he hadn't *sprung* it on you so suddenly, you would have accepted?'

'I don't know,' she said miserably. 'I meant to, but now I can never accept him.'

Impatiently, he swore under his breath and moved away from her, a few paces along the cliff, his back to her.

The wind lifted his hair and pulled the legs of his trousers against him so that they flapped at the ankles.

Rachel stood watching him, the aching misery inside her giving way to a strange sort of peace, and after a while he turned and came back to her.

Abruptly he asked, 'Why did you turn Watkins down?'

'What?' she said, the sudden question confusing her.

'Carl Watkins wrote you a letter offering to publish your poems,' he said sharply. 'Have you forgotten?'

'No, of course not. I didn't turn him down entirely.'

'You gave him permission to publish *one* in his anthology. Why did you refuse the book idea?'

It was growing rapidly dark and she could hardly see his face, but she had the impression he was glowering at her.

She turned away, starting to walk back to the house. 'I just decided I didn't want them published,' she said. 'Does it matter?'

'Yes, *damn* you, it does matter!' he said savagely, and grasped her shoulders to swing her round to stare up at him in the dim light. 'I went to a hell of a lot of trouble to sort those poems, and get them professionally typed, and take them to Carl. I persuaded him to read them and after various discussions he agreed they should be printed—*he* had to get his publisher to agree, and now you say you just don't want them published, after all. I came all this way to find out why, and you're going to find a better reason than that!'

'I'm sorry,' she said inadequately. 'I didn't know.'

'Didn't know what, for God's sake!'

'Well, that there was so much involved—typing and discussions . . .'

'Carl told you in his letter he'd discussed the whole thing with me.'

'Yes, I know, but—I thought you just—just handed them over. Well, you never *told* me anything!' she cried. 'I didn't even know you'd remembered my poems until I got his letter. You could have written!'

All her hurt misery came to the surface, and he stared down at her, trying to see her face in the gathering dark.

She swallowed and moved her gaze from his face to the blur of pale shirt between the lapels of his jacket. 'Two words isn't much,' she muttered resentfully.

'It was more than I got from you, however,' he reminded her.

'You didn't give me an address,' she said.

His hands gripped and almost shook her. 'Mrs Langholm had my address. Surely you knew that?'

'I didn't ask,' she said evasively.

Daman dropped his hands and said rather coldly, 'I hoped that in time you would stop hating me and want to know what was happening with your poems.'

'I don't hate you.'

There was a moment's silence before he said, 'I suppose that's something.'

Not understanding what he wanted from her, Rachel let that pass. They were walking again, and the smell of the sea drifted over the grass and mingled with the wet-earth scent of the land. A ghostly moon drove in and out of dark, high-flung clouds as their footfalls thudded softly on the ground.

'You couldn't have really thought I had forgotten your poems,' Damon said presently.

'Why not? You seemed to have forgotten me.'

'Now you're being ridiculous!' he snapped.

'And adolescent?'

She could have sworn she heard his teeth snap together as he walked beside her. Then he said, 'You certainly tempt me to spank you. Tell me why you decided not to publish, Rachel.'

'It didn't seem worth it,' she said. 'I sent some more off, after you left. They were rejected. And I'm not going to write any more.'

'*What?*'

'I *can't* write any more,' she explained. 'I tried, and they're no good.'

To her utter astonishment, he began to laugh. She stopped to stare at him a moment, and then turned to run away from his laughter, but he caught her hand and brought her up short.

'Rachel,' he said tenderly, 'you silly little nut, don't you know half the most famous poets and writers in the world could paper their houses with rejection slips? What did you say to me once, about "only one editor's opinion"?'

'But they *weren't* any good,' she insisted. 'I read them over after they came back, and they were so bad I threw them away. I tried some more, and I couldn't get them to come right. It just seemed to have dried up or something— I had ideas, but on paper they came out all wrong.'

'It's called writer's block,' he said. 'Don't worry about it —it will come right.'

'Will it?' she asked wistfully.

'I promise. Now, listen, you little idiot—can I tell Carl you've changed your mind? I'll want a signed letter from you before I go.'

'Does he really think they're worth publishing?' she asked doubtfully. 'He isn't doing it because he's a friend of yours?'

'My dear girl, Carl is a hard-headed editor. His boss is an even harder-headed publisher. Admittedly they don't expect to make a great deal on your book—I told you poetry isn't a great money-spinner, but it does have some prestige value, and believe me, they're not going to risk the reputation of their house just to do a favour for a friend.'

'Well, if you think I should——'

'I do. I'll type a letter tonight on my portable and get you to sign it in the morning. And shame on you, allowing a little thing like a rejection slip to throw you!'

'It wasn't only that,' she admitted. 'It was different when you were here. You understood about—writing. The Langholms don't, you see.'

'Do they disapprove? Or have you still not mentioned it? Surely you couldn't resist showing them your work in print—they're all the family you have.'

'Oh, yes, I showed them,' she said. 'They were pleased, but I think they thought it was a bit weird of me to have written it.'

'Yes, I see. The salt of the earth, the Langholms, but not poetry people.' He said abruptly, 'You realise that your position here is going to be impossible after tonight?'

'After what I did to Jerry——' she said soberly. 'If I had money, I'd go away and get a job. As it is, I suppose we'll all have to learn to live with it. Somehow.'

'I admire your guts,' he said drily. 'But that won't be easy—for any of you.'

'Especially Jerry,' she sighed with compunction. 'I wish I'd let it ride. I could have got hold of him later in private and——'

'That would only have made it worse,' said Damon. 'You were right to deny it on the spot. Your mistake was in deluding yourself that you could ever be happy married to a good-natured clod.'

'He isn't——'

'All right, he isn't. I don't want to listen to you telling me about young Jerry's virtues, if you don't mind.'

Rachel said, 'Oh——!' and turned her head, trying to see his expression. Her foot in its inadequate shoe fell on a patch of slippery mud, and she felt it slide under her and she clutched wildly at him, to save herself. His arms came round her and lifted her clear of the ground altogether for a moment before she found her feet again, leaning against him.

His hold didn't slacken, and into her hair she heard him say, 'I thought you were the one who could see your way in the dark.'

'I can,' she said on a soft laugh. 'But I didn't change my shoes.'

His jacket had fallen open as he grabbed at her, and she could feel the warmth of his chest against her cheek, and his heart beating against her breast. For a long, sweet moment they stayed like that, not moving, then she sighed softly and said, 'I miss you.'

Damon's hand stroked her hair, and then tugged at it gently until she raised her face. His kiss on her lips was tender, lingering but oddly restrained. Then he pushed her gently away and put his arm around her shoulders as they drew near the farmhouse.

They were still in the shadows beyond the porch light when he asked thoughtfully, 'Do you *want* to stay here?'

'After tonight?' she asked. 'I told you, if I had money for accommodation and travel, I'd leave and find a job.'

'If you want to leave,' he said, 'I'll take you tomorrow, if you like. There's room in my car—and in my home—and in my life ... Rachel?'

She was staring at him, his words hardly making sense, the deepening softness of his voice surely a trick of the night? Room in his *life*? For her?

'Do you mean—*marry* you?' she asked, as cautious joy spread within her.

There was a heart-stopping pause before he said, with a strange inflection, 'Yes. Why not?' as though he had only just thought of it, and her joy was extinguished in a sudden rush of embarrassed shame. Of course he hadn't meant marriage—he was joking or—he meant something rather less permanent than marriage. And she, with her idiotic naïveté, had jumped to conclusions.

'I'm sorry,' she said. 'Of course you don't mean it. There's no reason why you should——'

He caught her as she was about to turn to the house and pulled her into his arms. 'Of course I *do* mean it,' he snapped. 'For God's sake stop running away! Isn't *this* reason enough ...'

He found her mouth with his in a kiss that made no allowance for her inexperience. Her small, protesting movement was stilled almost before it had begun, and his arms held her inescapably against him while his mouth made a ruthless exploration of hers. His hand pushed aside her jacket and found the gentle swell of her breast, and as his mouth slackened its pressure a little he whispered against her lips, 'Marry me, Rachel. Say yes.'

'Yes—*Yes!*' Her yearning mouth found his again, but this time his kiss was devastatingly brief before he thrust her suddenly away.

In a voice harsh with emotion he said, 'That wasn't fair. If you want to change your mind in the morning, I'll understand. But I won't give you another chance like that.'

'I won't want it,' she said, quite certain. 'I love you, Damon.'

He thrust out his hand, and she put hers into it. He held her fingers tightly in his, and rubbed the back of her hand against his cheek, his skin rasping gently on hers. Then he turned her hand and dropped a quick kiss in the palm before releasing her.

'Still, we'll wait until morning,' he said. 'I don't think an announcement would be very tactful tonight.'

Jerry was not present when they returned to the lounge. Anne looked strained and Bert impassive, and the atmosphere was thick with unasked questions and ungiven answers.

Rachel went to sit by Anne on the sofa, whispering, 'I'm sorry, Auntie Anne.'

The older woman's lips were tight. 'Yes, well ... Jerry was very silly tonight, but I don't think you're entirely without blame, either, Rachel.'

'I know——'

'Well, we'll talk about it in the morning,' said Anne, glancing at Damon.

Evidently it was not to be discussed, even in lowered tones, before their guest. There was, Rachel thought, bound to be quite a lot of discussion in the morning, about one thing and another.

When morning came, she was scarcely prepared for it. Her eyes felt swollen and her head was dully aching. She had slept very little, and yet the events of the night before seemed unreal, like something she had dreamed.

Anne was vigorously banging pots about in the kitchen when Rachel joined her and began laying the table. It was seldom that any crisis was deemed serious enough to disrupt the normal routine of the household.

Evidently trying hard to be fair-minded, Anne said quietly as she stirred a big pot of porridge, 'I may have been mistaken, Rachel, but I thought you were encouraging Jerry.'

Concentrating on slicing bread for toast, Rachel answered, 'No, you weren't wrong, Auntie Anne. I really am sorry——'

'My dear, if you were annoyed at him blurting it out before he'd asked you properly, that's understandable, but he didn't deserve to be treated so—so badly last night. You'll both have apologies to make. Still, as long as you love each other——'

'I don't love Jerry in that way, Auntie Anne.' Rachel stopped slicing, her hand tightening on the handle of the knife. 'I thought I did, but last night I realised it wouldn't do. I can't marry Jerry.'

After a moment's pause, Anne said, 'You know, all couples have their ups and downs. It seems to me you and Jerry were very happy until last night. You make it up with him later, and you'll find he'll be only too happy to meet you half way. The poor boy is utterly miserable this morning, you know.'

She smiled encouragingly, and Rachel, miserable too, gritted her teeth momentarily and forced herself to speak again. 'Auntie Anne, please try to understand. I know I've behaved badly to Jerry, but I didn't mean to. I wish I could make it up to him, but I know I can't.' She took a deep breath and said, 'I'm going to go away. Today.'

Anne's hand on the wooden spoon halted its stirring. 'Don't be silly, dear. There's no need for that. Anyway, how would you go away?'

'With Damon.'

'Mr Curtis? Have you asked him?'

'You don't understand, Auntie Anne,' Rachel said quietly. 'I'm going to marry Damon.'

Unnoticed, the porridge was coagulating into thick lumps. Anne stared at Rachel as though trying to adjust to this completely unexpected idea.

'He wants to *marry* you? Is that why he came—why he asked to see you alone?'

'Not exactly.' Uneasily suppressing the knowledge that his proposal had seemed a spur-of-the-moment decision, Rachel explained, 'He wanted to talk about publishing some of my poetry, but we—he—well, we got talking about

other things, and he asked me to marry him.' That sounded
very vague, and when Anne cast a sharp glance at her and
said, 'Yes, and a bit more than talking, I'll be bound,' she
flushed a little and didn't answer.

Suddenly realising that the porridge was rapidly becoming a minor disaster, Anne lifted it hastily from the stove
and busied herself trying to rectify the results of her in-
attention.

'Well,' she said, tightlipped with disapproval, 'I must say
I'm extremely disappointed in you, Rachel. You had no
right to encourage poor Jerry to become serious about
you——'

'I know, Auntie Anne. I'm really sorry—I truly meant to
marry him, but——'

'But a famous writer is a better proposition than a plain
farm boy.' Anne suggested.

'I think "famous" is a slight exaggeration,' Damon's chill
voice said from the doorway. 'I take it Rachel has told you
she's going to marry me, Mrs Langholm. You don't seem
to approve.'

Slightly embarrassed, Anne rallied quickly. 'I must say
it's a bit of a shock, Mr Curtis. I had no idea anything like
that was going on between you and Rachel. For one thing,
you must be quite a lot older——'

'I am. And for that reason, nothing has been *going on*, as
you call it,' Damon said evenly. 'But I think you must know
that Rachel has potential which she can't fulfil here.'

'I don't know exactly what you mean by that, Mr Curtis.
My husband and I have done our best for Rachel since her
father died. If you mean university, she can go next year
if she wants to; she knows that, and we wouldn't stand in
her way. But I don't see what that has to do with marriage.
She's talking of going away with you this morning—well,
I can tell you my husband won't allow that. Rachel is very
young, and we're responsible for her. One thing I know,
you can't just get married on the spur of the moment. It
takes at least three days to fix the licence and the legal
angles. Rachel may be gullible enough to go with you, but
I'm afraid I can't let her do it.'

'I don't think you can stop her,' Damon said quietly, and Rachel saw an unmistakable gleam of humour in his eyes. 'I appreciate your concern, Mrs Langholm, but I can only assure you that the tactics of a nineteenth-century seducer are not mine. I fully intend to marry Rachel as soon as possible.'

'Then you can wait until you're married to take her away, can't you?'

Rachel said, 'Damon——' and he looked at her with expressionless eyes as Anne went on, 'I'm sure Rachel won't want to repay the trouble we've gone to in looking after her by going off with scarcely a decent goodbye, marriage or no marriage. She may have been thoughtless and silly, but she's a good girl, and I'm sure I can rely on her to do the right thing.'

'I thought you'd be glad,' said Rachel. 'I thought it would be easier for Jerry if I just went with Damon this morning.'

Anne's face softened a little. 'Well, of course it will be hard on Jerry. But right is right, and it wouldn't be right for you to run away to get married. There's no need, either. If you really want to marry Mr Curtis, we'll give you a proper wedding. After all we've done for you, Rachel, Uncle Bert and I would be very hurt if you were to just turn your back on us——'

'I wouldn't——' Distressed, Rachel stumbled over the words of reassurance and Damon interrupted.

'Perhaps you're right, Mrs Langholm,' he said smoothly, causing Rachel to turn an astonished face to him. He wasn't looking at her, but at her foster-mother, and his expression was bland and serious. 'Rachel was anxious not to cause Jerry any further embarrassment, and I'm afraid I selfishly took advantage of that, and tended to—er—sweep her off her feet. I have to return to Auckland today, I'm afraid—I'll be able to get a licence, and there are some other—matters —that perhaps should be attended to before the wedding. When would you suggest it should take place?'

Rachel felt disorientated. Surely Damon was being sarcastic? He *couldn't* seriously be joining forces with Auntie Anne to turn their marriage into a farcically conventional wedding day! She was certain that Damon would hate to be married before a flower-smothered altar with a bevy of bridesmaids and friends and relations turned out in their wedding finery to watch, and to eat and drink and laugh too much afterwards. He must have been aware that this was what Auntie Anne meant by a proper wedding.

'I don't want a big wedding,' she managed to say. 'I don't have any relatives, anyway.'

She wanted Damon to say, *Let's not wait, then*—but he wasn't looking her way, and Anne was saying soothingly, 'Of course, dear, but you'd like to look nice.'

'You'll be beautiful in white,' said Damon softly, and Rachel threw him a glance of pure hatred, certain he was mocking her. He raised his eyebrows, but she couldn't read the brief flicker of his glance. 'Would two weeks be long enough?' he asked Anne.

Tempted to scream, *I don't want to wait two weeks*! Rachel reminded herself to be adult and calm, and said, 'Is that necessary? I don't care about a dress——'

'Two weeks is not very long——' Anne was saying doubtfully. 'People will talk, you know.'

'Will they?' Damon said indifferently. 'But there won't be anything to talk about, will there?'

'A month, at least——' Anne said hesitantly.

Rachel said, 'No!'

'No?' Damon looked at her with a hint of laughter, and Anne with censure.

'Do *you* want to wait a month?' she asked Damon, demanding his answer.

He smiled and said, 'My darling, of course not. I'm trying not to be selfish and unreasonable.'

'Oh——' She made a tiny movement towards him, which was checked when Anne passed between them, saying resignedly as she poured lumpy porridge into plates, 'Well, two weeks, then. At least it will make things easier on poor Jerry.'

CHAPTER TEN

RACHEL didn't see Damon again until their wedding day. He phoned every night, the first time asking her if she had decided to change her mind. She answered a bald 'no' to the question, inhibited by the fact that the telephone was in the hall near the lounge and her end of the conversation would be audible to the Langholms.

She always answered the telephone with eager haste, only to become shy and tonguetied when she heard the sound of Damon's voice. The calls were never long, and Damon sounded crisp and indifferent rather than loverlike. He told her that the publishers were pleased she had consented to having her poems made into a book, and when she politely enquired after his own novel, he kept her up to date on its progress too. Because of the outstanding success of his last book, the publishers were eager to promote his next to the utmost, and he was busy with pre-publication arrangements as well as the preparations for the wedding. He seemed relieved when Rachel said she didn't want a honeymoon, and she guessed that it would not have been convenient for him to be going away at that time.

There had been one difficult interview with Jerry, during which she had tried inadequately to apologise and explain her behaviour, and he had looked at her as though she was some freak that he had never seen before. After that he had avoided her as much as possible, working long hours, and a few days before the planned wedding he went off with a friend for a pig-hunting expedition in the Urewera. Profoundly thankful to be relieved of his awkward presence, and still burdened by guilt, Rachel hoped after a week in the rugged mountain country with its mysterious rivers flowing over petrified forests buried in long-ago earthquakes, its ancient valleys of darkened, rain-wet native trees, and its rocky sandstone outcrops hiding caverns where bones of the extinct giant moa birds had been found, Jerry would be enabled to put their abortive affair into perspective and perhaps forgive her in time.

Anne took her to Napier to choose her wedding dress, and with difficulty Rachel managed to hold out for a simple little dress in white crepe georgette with a skirt that flowed softly to a point above her ankles and no ornamentation at all. 'Damon will like it,' she said in answer to Anne's protests that it was too plain for a wedding dress. 'It's a small wedding, anyway.'

She washed her hair the night before the wedding and answered Damon's call with her head swathed in a towel. He was staying in the only hotel in the town, and made her laugh with his description of the patrons of the bar. 'I'm inviting them all to the wedding,' he said solemnly. 'In uniform, of course.' Since he had described the 'uniform' as rubber boots, black singlets and shorts of indeterminate origin and colour, the thought of Damon's newfound drinking mates all turning up at the tiny church thus attired, and Anne's consternation, made Rachel begin to laugh again. 'We'll have a guard of honour of crossed cowshed brooms,' Damon added.

When he said, 'I'll see you tomorrow,' she caught her breath and said, 'I wish you'd come here.'

'So do I,' he told her. 'But your Aunt Anne was adamant it wouldn't be right. A very rightminded lady, Mrs Langholm—and determined, too.'

'Yes, I know.' Rachel had a strong feeling that Damon could cope quite easily with any number of strong-minded ladies, and the suspicion gained strength when he added, 'I wish you'd told me how you felt. I thought you shared her superstition.'

'I'm not superstitious.'

'I'm glad to hear it. We still have a lot to learn about each other, don't we?'

'Yes.' Suddenly shy again, she said, echoing him, 'I'll see you tomorrow, then.'

His subtly possessive, 'Goodnight, my darling,' echoed in her ears after he had rung off.

She wound her hair up into a soft coil and pinned it with shaking fingers, tried and discarded the coronet of fabric roses that Anne had insisted on buying for a headdress.

Anne hovered impatiently behind her, tucking in wisps of hair and picking up the wreath of roses again to arrange it.

'There,' she said, stepping back. 'That's nice. Although I don't see why you wouldn't have a veil——'

Rachel looked at herself and remembered Damon saying, '*I'll never give you roses,*' and the petals of the jasmine scenting the night.

'No,' she said firmly, removing the roses. 'It isn't me, Auntie Anne. I'm sorry, but it doesn't feel right.'

'But, *Rachel!*' Anne wailed in exasperation. 'You must have something!'

Rachel rose and kissed her cheek, smiling faintly. 'Just wait a minute, Auntie Anne.'

She left the room and came back with her hands full of jasmine, and tucked one starry spray into the shining chignon at the back of her head. The cool blossoms trembled against her hair and kissed her neck, and the remainder trailed from her hand in a graceful fall against her dress.

'Well——' Anne said doubtfully. 'Well, it's very pretty. But fresh flowers wilt, dear.'

'Never mind, they'll last until the wedding is over,' Rachel grinned youthfully, quite spoiling the sophisticated effect of her smooth hairstyle.

Noting it, Anne said involuntarily, 'Are you sure you know what you're doing, dear? We hardly know the man, after all ...'

'I know him,' Rachel said quietly, with confidence. As Damon had said, they had much to learn about each other, but their minds knew each other, had touched each other with love.

They touched again when she walked into the small,

shabby church and saw him waiting for her before the altar, and he turned and swept one comprehensive, silver-grey glance over her, and then smiled. She saw his hand move and clench as though he had been going to hold it out to her before she had even reached his side, and in her hand the jasmine stopped trembling as she walked steadily to stand by him.

Afterwards he kissed her fleetingly, but his hand was tight on hers as they posed on the church step for the professional photographer Anne had hired.

He had invited no guests, and Rachel had allowed Anne to invite only her own family and the families of their farm workers and the nearest neighbours. It added up to just over a dozen people in all, and rather than go back to the station, they had arranged to have a meal at the hotel where Damon was staying, in the small private bar. Later Rachel was shown to a room where she changed into a natural-coloured skirt and jacket in light wool with a silk blouse. She thought it made her look both smart and more mature. The jasmine petals were already looking tired as she removed the spray from her hair. They had been unseasonable, anyway, blooming in the shelter of the warm, sun-filled little porch.

She took one tiny bloom and pressed it carefully between the leaves of the small prayerbook she had used in church. It had her mother's name on the front flyleaf, the only memento she had excepting the photograph which was now packed into the bottom of her new suitcase, which Bert had already transferred to the boot of Damon's car.

They left amid a shower of confetti and conventional good wishes to which Damon responded with good grace. A few miles down the road he stopped the car and they got out and brushed away the confetti as much as they could.

'You've got it in your hair,' Damon said, carefully picking tiny coloured flakes from the soft strands. 'You'll have to let it down. I can't get it all out.'

'Oh—and it took me ages to fix it,' she mourned as she removed the pins and shook out her hair. 'There—is it all gone?'

'Yes. I like your hair loose. Lovely things shouldn't be confined.'

'Oh. Didn't you like it, in church?'

'You looked lovely,' he said gently. 'Very, very beautiful.'

'Auntie Anne insisted on white,' she explained rather self-consciously.

'I thought you were complying with *my* preference on that,' he said. 'Were you warm enough in that flimsy-looking thing?'

'Yes, thank you. It isn't as thin as it looked. And that *flimsy-looking thing* was my wedding dress,' she reminded him with conscious dignity. 'Every girl's dream,' she added, tongue in cheek.

He laughed and said, 'You constantly surprise me, Rachel. Anyway, as one of the few who are really entitled to wear it, why shouldn't you have your white wedding dress?'

They were standing close, looking at each other and smiling. His hands came up to rest lightly on her waist, sliding under the open jacket to her back until she could feel their warmth through her blouse. Willingly she leaned against him, her hands resting on his chest, her face lifted for his kiss, but he waited, looking down at her, the smile still faintly etching his mouth. Then his mouth lowered to hers briefly in a gentle, exploratory kiss, but it wasn't enough for her, and she put up her hands around his neck and clung until the kiss deepened with passion and his arms tightened so that she could hardly breathe.

His hands moved to her head, and his lips left hers as he deliberately tipped back her head and his mouth ran down the length of her smooth throat to the open neckline of her blouse. His arm slipped down to encircle her waist and she leaned back on it as he began to unfasten her blouse, watching his strong, sure fingers through half-closed eyes.

But the sound of a car approaching the bend in the road made her stiffen and thrust him away, instinctively pulling the edges of her blouse together.

The car roared by with a flurry of loose metal, and
Damon laughed down at her flushed face and said, 'Not the
time or the place, Mrs Curtis. Never mind, we have plenty
of time.'

She got into the car and began to fumble with the
buttons, but before she had done up the last, at the top,
he had slid in beside her and was gently pushing her hand
down, saying. 'Let me.'

He grasped the fabric and pushed it aside with his
thumb, dropping a quick kiss on the exposed curve of her
breast and smiling into her shyly surprised eyes as he
fastened the button over it. Just for a moment his hand
lingered there warmly before he turned to switch on the
ignition.

This was another kind of knowing, she thought as she
watched his hands on the wheel and remembered the feel
of them on her body. All of it was a part of their growing
knowledge of each other, and this part was going to be the
strangest and the most exciting.

In Napier they stopped for an hour, to have a snack and a
drink and stroll along the famous Marine Parade with its
majestically tall Norfolk pines marching along in line with
the road and the long, straight beach. They stopped to
gaze at the bronze statue of Pania, gazing wistfully out to
sea, and to read the memorial plaque that recorded the
determination of the people of the city to rebuild their
home after the terrible earthquake of 1931.

    '... and I,
    in faith, shall build my towers toward the sun——
    A stronger city than was there before.'

Rachel shivered as she turned away after reading the final
lines, gazing down the steeply shelving, shingly beach, and
wondering how it had felt that sultry day so long ago,
when the beach had been lined with patients wheeled out
from a badly damaged hospital—patients who had lain
watching helplessly as from the heaving sea a huge tidal
wave raced inexorably towards the shore; only to be saved
at the last moment as the sea-bed itself rose up in a

tremendous upheaval and blocked the wave so that it curled back on itself and receded.

'Don't be morbid,' Damon chided gently, his arm lightly encircling her waist.

'Do you know what I'm thinking?'

'Just now, yes. I can see it in your face. It's a long time ago, and the town was rebuilt—it's even a better town, by all accounts.'.

'Oh, yes. They widened the streets and built the Marine Parade with the rubble from the ruined buildings. And the lifting of the sea-bed drained land that would have taken years to reclaim—ten thousand acres, that allowed the city to expand. But I've met people who lived through it, and it must have been terrifying. After the main shocks the ground kept heaving and rolling for days. There was a bus that ran into a crack that opened in the road and almost swallowed it.'

'It must have been like the end of the world.'

'Yes. It was, for some. Some people were never found afterwards.'

He dropped a light kiss on her temple and said, turning her away from the harbour and its slow, booming waves, 'Come on, we have a long way to go.'

He had asked her during one of their rather stilted telephone conversations if she would prefer to stay the night at Taupo or further along their way to Auckland, but Rachel had said that in spite of the long journey, she preferred to travel all the way to his home—which was to be hers too, now.

They returned to the car and drove on. The weather was cool and fine, and when they reached the bleak Desert Road, high and windswept with its brown tussock grass barely covering the grey shingle, they had clear, spectacular views of the three snow-covered volcanoes, Tongariro, Ngauruhoe and Ruapehu, standing white and proud against the blue sky. From the almost perfect cone of Ngauruhoe a faint wisp of white volcanic smoke emerged, a reminder that the volcanoes were not extinct, but capable of erupting at any time.

Seeing her looking curiously at the smoke, Damon asked, 'Do you know the story of the mountains?'

Rachel shook her head.

'A chief called Ngatoro-i-rangi is supposed to have got caught in a snowstorm on one of the mountains. He was almost dying of the cold, and prayed for the fire of the gods. When they sent it, he was so grateful he sacrificed a female slave who was his companion on the journey, by throwing her into the crater of Ngauruhoe. The mountain is named after her.'

Rachel made a disgusted face, and he laughed. 'Sorry, Rachel, perhaps I shouldn't have mentioned the last bit. You're too sensitive.'

'I hope the gods appreciated the sacrifice,' she said.

'Well, their fire stayed in the mountains. But gifts from the gods tend to be two-edged swords. Volcanoes are tricky to deal with. One day I'll take you skiing on Ruapehu, and we'll swim in the crater lake. It's hot, and quite an experience in the midst of the snow.'

'I can't ski,' she confessed.

'You can learn.'

'Will you teach me?'

He glanced at her with meaning, saying, 'I'm going to teach you a lot, Rachel. I promise you'll enjoy it.'

She looked away, shying from his eyes, and he put out his hand and grasped one of hers as he drove. His hand was warm and firm, and the knuckles pressed against her thigh with a delicious, sweet intimacy. She leaned sideways to rest her cheek against his shoulder, but after a while he had to change gear as the road wound up a slope, and she sat up as he took his hand away.

At Taupo they skirted the lake, passing the clusters of fishing huts at the water's edge that eventually gave way to more substantial fishermen's lodges, and then to rows of motels, before they reached the town with its wide streets and big old trees. The tranquil inland sea lapped gently at the shingle-sand of the narrow shore at the foot of the main street, a few children bravely paddling in the cold shallows.

At Wairakei Damon stopped the car and let Rachel gaze with some awe at the steam-filled valley where the geothermal activity had been at least partially harnessed to the service of humans in their search for sources of electricity. The combination of steam hissing out of natural apertures in the ground and huge coils of pipes snaking among the sluphur-laden outcrops of rock and the dried, grey manuka scrub, was weird, like some sort of science-fiction landscape.

'It looks sinister,' she said, smiling at her own reactions. But Damon agreed. Watching a workman in a yellow hard hat walk confidently across the constantly trembling earth, to be quickly obscured by steam, and listening to the muted roar that was a constant feature of the place, he said, 'I know what you mean. I don't think I'd care to work here myself.'

When they reached Rotorua it was dark and had begun to rain, but the green lights of the street lamps revealed numbers of small cairns by the roadside that covered deep holes from which columns and wisps of steam emerged. Here the earth's crust was so thin that constant volcanic and geothermal activity gave many homes their hot water from natural springs in their properties, and almost every one of the numerous hotels offered its own thermal hot pool.

They had dinner at one of the bigger hotels, and Rachel unexpectedly found herself surprisingly hungry. Damon ordered wine to go with their meal, and she had an unaccustomed two glasses. At first it made her sparkle, and she found herself flirting with her new husband and enjoying it, revelling in the look she could bring to his eyes with a touch of her hand or a promising, smiling glance. But when they climbed back into the car she was suddenly overwhelmingly sleepy, and dropped off into a deep slumber soon after they left the city.

In the hours that followed she wakened occasionally to stare out at the rainswept darkness and sleepily watch the windscreen wipers sweeping back and forth across the glass in front of her, the raindrops sometimes garishly outlined by the street lights of the small towns that they passed through. In the darkness she could see Damon's strong profile and sometimes watch him pleasurably as he concentrated on driving them safely through the night, his hands steady and confident on the wheel.

Once he reached into the back seat and found a light rug which he threw over her, and she gratefully snuggled into its warmth, resisting the temptation to lean her head on his shoulder as drowsiness overtook her again. In the darkness and the wet, he needed freedom for his hands to manage the car, and no distractions.

As they sped along the southern motorway into the city of Auckland she roused herself and tried to peer out the window, but her curiosity could not be satisfied by a ribbon of wet road and occasional glimpses of rows of houses lining it. When they left the motorway and began driving more slowly through the central city streets, the better lighting enabled her to see the modern shops and office buildings that lifted their glass and metal façades to the sky with breathtaking confidence. After the squat, low look of most of the buildings in Napier, and knowing that Auckland was not entirely free from the occasional earth tremor, she couldn't help a small exclamation of apprehension at their height.

Glancing at her staring upwards through the window, Damon said, 'They build them big, now. With new techniques they're supposed to be quite able to stand up to a shock or two.'

'So they say,' she said doubtfully. 'There are a few taller buildings in Napier, too, now.'

Briefly they drove along near the waterfront, the lights along the shore reflected brokenly in the darkened waters of the harbour, and the arch of the harbour bridge which spanned its further reaches outlined against the darkness in orange lights.

Damon swung the car into a side street and turned into a driveway hung with trees that brushed the roof of the car as they traversed its short length to the carport where he finally stopped.

'Welcome home,' he said softly, turning to Rachel and lightly kissing her cheek.

She climbed out without waiting for him to open her door, but he was beside her in a moment, locking it while she stood waiting. The rain had stopped, but a gentle dripping from the shrubs growing in front of the block of town houses mingled with the distant sound of traffic. Damon got their cases from the boot of the car and led the way inside. Stopping outside a panelled door he put down the luggage and taking out his key, said, 'Shall I carry you over the threshold?'

'No, thanks.' She was about to add something light and teasing when he swung open the door and fumbled for a light switch, illuminating a small vestibule carpeted in a rick dark brown, where a small table stood on an oriental rug, holding a crystal vase of yellow roses.

Glancing at them, Damon commented, 'Mrs Baker has done her stuff, I see.' Seeing her puzzled glance, he said, 'Haven't I mentioned her? She comes in once a week to spruce the place up. I asked her to give it a special do this time, and she must have taken it to heart. I don't think the vase is mine—she's probably lent it for the occasion.'

He shut the outside door, deposited the cases in a corner of the little vestibule, and pushed open the far door. 'Come in,' he said, smiling at her.

Rachel noticed that the light was on in the other room, and wondered if Mrs Baker had left it for them. Damon seemed to see it at the same time, and as she walked past him, he was turning his head to the room with a puzzled frown. He suddenly drew in his breath behind her as she stopped just inside the doorway, surprised and confused.

It was quite a big room, with side lights bathing its obvious comfort and moderate luxury in a gentle, relaxing glow. There seemed to be a colour scheme of soft greens and blues with a few touches of dusky pink, and on a long pale blue sofa, resting her head on a couple of cushions, was a woman dressed in a silky gown with flowing sleeves edged with lace. The gown was deep pink and although it didn't fit the description of what Rachel thought of as a negligee, it was obviously some sort of nightwear. Dark hair flowed over the woman's shoulders in some disarray, and a magazine lay open on her lap. She had turned her head at their entrance and was looking at them with slightly raised, finely arched brows over very blue eyes.

For a long moment it was as though time stood still, the three of them caught in a tableau.

Then beside Rachel, Damon's voice, harsh with anger, ripped out at the woman. 'What the *hell* are you doing here?'

'Damon *darling*!' she smiled with apparent amusement. 'Waiting for you, obviously. But I seem to be somewhat superfluous.' Looking at Rachel's shocked immobility, she stood up in a sinuous, graceful movement. 'I'm sorry, dear,' she said kindly. 'He should have made sure he was off with his old love before he got on with the new one, shouldn't he?' She stretched herself delicately, and the satin fabric stretched over her full breasts, making it obvious she was wearing nothing underneath it.

'That's not funny, Paula!' Damon snapped. 'How did you get in?'

The woman cast an apologetic glance at Rachel. 'With the key that you gave me, of course, darling. When you threw me out last week, you forgot to ask for it back.'

'I didn't throw you out.'

'Politely asked me to leave, then. You should have explained why you wanted me out, Damon. I would have understood.'

Damon thrust past Rachel and said with controlled force, 'Well, understand this. You can't stay here. Pack your bag and I'll call you a taxi.'

He went to a telephone standing on a table by the wall and picked up the receiver, beginning to dial.

Paula made a little face, turning to Rachel. 'Forceful, isn't he?' she drawled. 'Shall we introduce ourselves? Since Damon doesn't seem to be going to do it. I'm Paula Winfield.'

Damon slammed down the receiver, only halfway through dialling. 'For God's sake, Paula, will you shut up and pack. Rachel is my wife!'

For the first time, Paula's composure slipped just a trifle. But she quickly recovered from the momentary shock which showed in her face and said, 'My dear—really? I had no idea.' Turning to Damon, who was grimly dialling again, she said, 'I suppose congratulations are in order. Am I the first to know?'

'No.' He turned away and began speaking into the telephone, ordering a taxi. 'Twenty minutes,' he said, crisply. Then, turning to Paula, 'Where would you like to go?'

Paula shrugged. 'The YWCA? The Salvation Army, perhaps?'

'Don't be ridiculous!' He barked the name of a hotel into the phone, and putting it down began to use the phone book.

'Twenty minutes, the man says,' Paula remarked conversationally to Rachel. She moved towards a door through which Rachel could see a double bed with a gold and white brocade spread half turned back, and going through, pushed it half-to. She could be heard moving about as Damon spoke again into the phone, reserving a hotel room.

He put down the receiver and seeing Rachel still standing by the door, said, 'For heaven's sake sit down, Rachel!'

She cast him a blind look and obeyed, avoiding the sofa and seating herself gingerly on one of the large, soft armchairs.

He thrust a hand over his hair and said, 'I'm sorry, I didn't mean to snap at you—*God*, I'm sorry about this!'

She said nothing, looking at him as though he was a rather odd stranger.

He took a step towards her, saying roughly, '*Rachel*, don't——'

He was interrupted by Paula, coming out of the bedroom to say plaintively, 'Damon, I can't shut my case. Would you mind——'

Furiously he turned, biting off an exasperated exclama-

tion. As he strode past her, he muttered in a low, savage
voice, 'Did you have to use that room?'

'But naturally——' she said, with a helpless little shrug
as she followed him. In the doorway she turned to Rachel,
saying with a conspiratorial air, 'He's got a frightful temper,
dear. Or have you found that out already?'

Rachel just stared, unable to reply, but noting with some
part of her mind, in minute detail, the woman's appearance.
She had changed into a fine jersey dress in a shade of violet
that made her blue eyes look darker and mysterious. High-
heeled shoes emphasised slim ankles and perfect legs, and
her dark hair clung to her shoulders in glossy waves. She
was very beautiful and obviously a sexy, sophisticated
woman.

She leaned against the doorjamb, watching Damon who
had disappeared into the room out of Rachel's sight. When
he appeared, carrying a small white case, and thrusting a
fur-collared coat and a black handbag into Paula's hand, she
took them from him with an air of resignation. He dug in
his pocket and took out several notes which he handed to
her. 'That should pay for the hotel for a few days,' he said
coldly.

'Thoughtful of you,' she said mockingly. 'I'll pay you
back when I'm working again.'

'That isn't necessary,' he said stiffly.

'Oh, but I insist. Whatever will your new little wife
think——'

'*Shut up!*' he ground savagely, and took her arm in a
hard grip. 'I'll see you out. I think your taxi has just arrived.'

'Well—goodbye, dear,' said Paula as she walked past
Rachel's chair. 'I wish you joy of him!'

Rachel's lips somehow answered for her with an almost
soundless, stiff goodbye.

When they had gone out she got up from the chair and
walked around the room, her numbed mind gradually returning to life. There was an ornamental brick archway at
one end leading to a dining area and a small functional
kitchen. She shied away from the door of the bedroom and

opened another which proved to be also a bedroom, with twin beds in it and another door which led into a bathroom. The bathroom had another door which she opened and found herself looking into the first bedroom again. The curtains matched the bedspread and there was a luxurious long-pile white rug on the carpeted floor. It was a very beautiful room.

Quickly she closed the door and returned to the other room. It had a window looking out to the back of the house, and she turned and tried to see out, but in the darkness there was no view.

She heard Damon return to the living room and call her name. She didn't answer, but he came into the room and she felt him come up behind her. A shiver ran down her back and she stiffened as his hands tentatively touched her shoulders.

'Rachel, I don't know what to say.' She heard him say, low-voiced.

'I think it might be best if you didn't say anything,' she told him thinly. 'This is a nice room. If you don't mind, I'd like to sleep here tonight.'

There was a long pause, and then he said, 'Yes, of course. I'll get your case.'

She heard him move away, and forced herself to turn away from the window so that she was facing him when he came back. But when he appeared in the doorway, she kept her gaze on the case that he put down on the carpet by one of the twin beds. She couldn't meet his eyes.

He straightened and thrust his hands into his pockets, standing before her. Then he took them out and made a movement towards her.

Without even thinking about it, Rachel stepped back.

His movement checked, he said, standing rock-still, 'You're entitled to an explanation.'

Jerkily, she shook her head. 'Please, Damon. I'm very tired.'

After a pause he said, 'Yes. If it means anything, I wasn't intending to claim my marital rights tonight.'

'How considerate of you,' she said bitterly, and drew in

a sharp breath as he made a sudden movement, but it was quickly stopped.

He turned on his heel, muttering a low-voiced, 'Goodnight,' and closed the door sharply behind him.

CHAPTER ELEVEN

RACHEL woke with an unaccustomed sensation of dread. In the first few seconds she recalled the nightmarish events of the last hour of her wedding day, and wished passionately that she had never woken.

She also recalled the casual way that Damon had first asked her to marry him, and her conviction at the time that he had not really intended her to take him seriously.

How very stupid she had been, she thought now. Writhing with hurt humiliation, she made herself look at their relationship objectively and examine the events which had led up to their marriage.

From the first, Damon had found her physically attractive, but too young for him. Whatever he had meant by his first offer to take her away with him, it had not been marriage. Only her naïve assumption that he was proposing had made him entertain the idea, and perhaps the notion had appealed to him as a way of appeasing his conscience. She remembered very clearly now that even when she had innocently declared her love for him, he had not reciprocated. At the time, his loving gesture had been enough to assure her he returned her feelings, but now his omission of the actual words disturbed her.

His insistence that she could change her mind, which she had stupidly assumed was a mark of his concern for her happiness, now took on a different light. Had he been halfhoping that she would back out, after all, and let him off the hook? He was too fond of her to hurt her by jilting her himself, but perhaps he had already begun to regret the impulse which had made him agree to her suggestion of marriage.

That fact—that it was she who had first mentioned the

word marriage—lacerated her pride in the light of her new knowledge. No wonder he had agreed to a postponement of their wedding day so willingly! His mistress had still been ensconced in his home, and he had needed time to get rid of her before he brought his bride here.

It was all so sordid, and made worse by the callous way he had treated Paula last night. Shivering, Rachel wondered if one day he would look at her with that cold rage, that utter indifference to her feelings. She hoped that if he did, she would put as brave a face on it as Paula had.

Absorbed in her frantic thoughts, she hardly heard the knock on the door. When Damon opened it and walked into the room, holding a cup and saucer in his hand, she sat up swiftly and the sheet fell away to reveal the low-necked satin nightgown she had donned unthinkingly the night before.

Damon's eyes slipped from her face to her body, and she snatched at the sheet, bringing a slight, amused smile to his mouth. He was dressed in close-fitting trousers and a long-sleeved shirt casually open at the neck.

'I've brought you a cup of tea,' he said, approaching the bed.

'Thank you.' Her voice worked automatically, but she felt paralysed, unable to reach out and take the cup from his hand. She looked up at his face, so familiar, and yet this morning she felt she was looking at a complete stranger.

He stood for a moment, then placed the cup and saucer on the bedside table and shoved his hands into his pockets, his mouth losing its smile and assuming a faintly grim look.

'I won't leap on you if you let the sheet drop,' he promised gently. 'Or is that death-grip you have on it because you can't bear to take your cup of tea from my hands?'

'Don't be silly,' she muttered, taking the cup and cradling it in her hands, looking down into the wavering fluid.

'Drink it while it's hot,' he advised, with a faint undercurrent of irritation in his tone.

Rachel sipped at it and said, 'It was kind of you to bring it.'

'I aim to be a considerate husband,' he said, and glancing at the rather brooding mockery in his face, she knew he was reminding her of the 'rights' he had not claimed last night.

Her hands tightened on the cup and she took a gulp of hot tea and blinked tears away from her eyes.

Damon stood there in silence until she had finished, and then the cup was gently taken from her and replaced on the saucer. Her hands closed tightly on the edge of the sheet again as he sat on the side of the bed, his hands resting on either side of her.

She kept her eyes down, seeing the silver buckle on his belt, the small white shirt button above it. He moved his hand and took one of hers, prying it away from the bed-clothes, taking her reluctant fingers in his. He raised her hand to his mouth and pressed a long kiss on her knuckles, and she said sharply, 'Don't!'

He dropped her hand and cupped her chin with his, forcing her to look at him. His eyes were brilliant with an emotion—or a mixture of emotions—that she was too in-experienced to identify.

'Right,' he said in clipped tones. 'Explanations first, is it?'

Suddenly in a panic, Rachel lifted a clenched fist and knocked away his hand, sure that explanations would only humiliate her further, knowing that if he put into words the fact that he had asked her to marry him on a sudden whim, prompted by nothing more than fondness and a desire to spare her hurt, she could not help but cry. 'No!' she said. 'I don't want to hear any explanations.' Suddenly resent-ment flamed in her, and she welcomed it, because anger would banish the tears that threatened.

'That should be good news,' said Damon. 'If it means you trust me enough not to require an explanation.' He scanned her face, his eyes wary and narrowed suddenly. 'But some-how I don't think that's what you mean, is it?'

Sudden pain hit her, as she realised that she desperately wanted to trust him, that her love should be equal to this acid test. But there was no reassurance in his face, only a hard, sardonic mockery. No tenderness—no love. She had hardly seen him since they decided to be married, and before that not for months—they had not even corresponded after he had dropped out of her life when the summer was ending. Anne had been right when she said that they hardly knew this man. How foolishly young it seemed now, her assertion that *she* knew him. Always she had known that his was a complex personality, and she had known only one of the many facets of it.

What was in her bruised heart found an echo in her voice. 'I—hardly know you,' she said. 'How do I know if I can believe your—excuses?'

His hand slid down and encircled her throat, and the glitter in his eyes frightened her. '*Excuses?*' he said softly. 'I don't deal in *excuses*, Rachel. Only facts.'

Fright making her angry again, she said, 'I don't think anything could explain the *fact* that your mistress was here waiting for you on your wedding night.'

Coldly he said, '*Ex*-mistress, actually. Are you going to listen to the rest, now?'

'No!' She twisted away from him with an effort, burying her head in the pillows behind her, and dramatically putting her palms over her ears. 'Go away!' she cried, her voice muffled into the pillow. 'Leave me alone!'

'*Rachel!*' Hard hands captured her wrists and pulled them down, wrenched her around to face him again, her head against the pillow, her hands imprisoned against the mattress as he leaned over her. She flinched from the cold fury in his face. 'All right,' he said. 'I'm not going to grovel, Rachel. I won't force explanations on you that you don't want to hear, either.' His mouth twisted. 'It's going to be an odd kind of marriage——'

'It's not going to be a marriage at all!' Rachel almost spat at him, and then tried ineffectually to press back in the pillow at the look in his face, the sudden utter stillness of him.

'Just what do you mean by that?' he asked, very softly. But it was a softness that brought a faint shiver spiralling up her spine.

Bravely, she swallowed, and said, 'I'm leaving.'

'The hell you are.' He still didn't move, but she was very conscious of the strength of the hands that held her, the hard set of his mouth as he leaned over her. *'For better, for worse,'* he quoted. *'Till death us do part.'*

'No. It—isn't a real marriage yet, anyway.'

'What's that supposed to mean?' he asked slowly.

'I mean we could still get an annulment.'

A brief flicker that might have been amusement leapt and died in his eyes. 'Or we could make it a real marriage,' he said. Watching the quick alarm in her eyes he smiled sardonically and added, 'It seems I made a mistake last night.'

He lowered his head slowly, and she lay as though paralysed with fear until his lips feathered lightly against hers. The touch galvanised her into movement, and she whipped her head aside, crying *'No!'*

'You say no an awful lot, my lovely,' he muttered, his mouth moving against the skin of her neck. He moved so that he was lying on the bed, his chest pressing against her breasts, one leg imprisoning hers. Hampered by the blankets, she tried to kick him off without success. She felt his tongue tracing the groove of her jaw and neck, and stopping below her ear, and her body's automatic response made her clench her teeth in determined rejection. Damon gave a soft laugh and asked, 'Do you like that?'

Moving her head, trying to get away from him, she said, 'Does Paula?'

Her eyes momentarily challenged his before he took advantage of her movement and brought his mouth down on hers in a long, angry kiss that was barely short of brutality.

Rachel lay helpless under the onslaught, willing not to cry. She knew that he had meant to be gentle, until she had taunted him with Paula's name. If he went through with it, it was better this way, even if he hurt her. To have him evoke a willing response from her would have been the ultimate humiliation. If he was angry and rough she could fight him, even though she was bound to lose. She would make it a sour victory for him. But if she let him calculatedly use his greater expertise and experience at lovemaking to make her not only submit but respond, her capitulation would be utter and complete, and her pride trampled in the dust.

When he lifted his mouth, his eyes glittering into hers, her lips felt swollen, and her breathing was fast. He let go one of her hands and began to unbutton his shirt, and when she tried to hit at him, he fended her off with a hard arm that bruised hers against him, and said, 'Stop fighting, Rachel.'

'*I won't!*' She lifted her hand again, but he caught it, and with a hard laugh, he moved so that both her wrists were imprisoned in his right hand and held against his chest, left bare by the unbuttoned shirt. Her fingers moved convulsively, trying to scratch at him, but his grip tightened so painfully at the touch of her nails that she had to stop.

His left hand went to her shoulder and eased down the narrow strap of her nightdress, and there was nothing she could do as the thin fabric slipped down from her breast and Damon lowered his dark head again and touched his mouth to the creamy-gold softness of her skin, and his warm hard hand replaced the light softness of the satin against her body.

His leg pressed against her thighs, the heat of his desire penetrating through the blankets, and when he moved deliberately so that she could feel him wanting her, she was suddenly young and frightened and very much out of her depth.

'Please, Damon,' she gasped, her throat tight with tears. 'Please—please *stop*!'

He didn't look at her, but his mouth left her breast and moved to within a hairsbreadth of the small hollow at the base of her throat.

'I don't want to stop,' he said, the thickness in his voice making her heart bump with fright.

She whispered, 'Please, Damon—I'll hate you.'

Slowly he lifted his head to look at her. 'What difference would it make?' he asked. 'If you're leaving me?' He released her wrists and as quickly imprisoned her hands between them as he snaked his hand into her hair, holding her head tilted to his kiss. 'What's the bloody difference?' he asked, before his mouth ravaged hers again, ruthlessly parting her lips, his breath invading her, his tongue edging along her teeth until she tried to snap them, and he withdrew, looking down at her with a mixture of anger and a sort of reluctant appreciation.

'Don't,' she said, not knowing herself if it was a warning or a plea.

He took a deep breath, seeming to gather himself in some way. 'What if I don't?' he asked, his voice quite hard and even. 'Will you stay?'

She hesitated, and he suddenly caught her wrists again and leaned the full weight of his body against the length of hers. 'Well?'

'I'll stay,' she said at last. 'If you promise not to touch me.'

His face hardened. 'Nothing doing, Rachel.'

Her fear must have shown in her face. He released her wrists and caught at her shoulders, dropping his head to the curve of her neck. 'Oh, God! What a child you are!' his muffled voice muttered below her ear. 'I can't promise not to touch you, darling, but I promise I won't rape you.'

He lifted his head then and looked at her. 'Fair enough?'

Choked with relief, she nodded warily.

'And you promise to stay?'

'I promise.'

He lifted his hand and smoothed a wisp of hair away from her cheek, then bent to her mouth. Rachel closed her eyes as he took a long, sweet and tender kiss, but she didn't respond, her body remaining stiff and unyielding under his. When he rolled off the bed she kept her eyes shut and raised an arm to shield her face from his gaze.

He took her hand in a firm but not cruel hold and pulled it away, and she opened her eyes, trying to veil the emotion in them. He was inspecting her face with concentration, trying to find tears, she guessed, and was glad that her eyes were quite dry.

She wasn't sure why he wanted her to stay. Perhaps it had something to do with pride and losing face. Perhaps to do with desire or even the pride of possession. Or maybe he was challenged by her refusal to give in to him. There was a hint of speculation in his eyes as he watched her pull up the straps of her gown.

He had refused a promise not to touch her, and she guessed he hoped that she would eventually give in to his practised lovemaking. Stubbornly, she was determined not to. The battle lines were drawn.

'Don't look so tragic,' said Damon, picking up the cup and saucer from the table beside her. 'You could call it our first marital row.'

He left the door ajar as he left the room, and she could hear him in the kitchen, rattling crockery with some savagery. He must have known, as she did with every bone of her body, that this was something much more fundamental and potentially damaging than a petty honeymoon quarrel.

When she had got up and dressed she made her bed, smoothing the cover carefully until she realised that she was filling in time to put off the moment when she would have to face Damon again.

She went into the living room and could see the other bedroom through the open door, the bed still unmade. She hesitated, and then Damon came out of the kitchen, casting her a rather sharp look, and asked, 'What would you like to do today?'

'What is there to do?' she asked, and avoided his sardonic look at that.

'I expect you'd prefer to go out,' he said. 'Shall I give you a guided tour of the city?'

'That would be nice.'

He laughed softly at her prim politeness, but she was grateful to him for suggesting they go out. The tension in the house would have been hard to dispel if they had spent the day there.

He drove her first to the top of Mount Eden, one of the city's dormant volcanic cones, giving a wide, sweeping view of the city and the harbour with the gentle slopes of Rangitoto island rising from its calm waters. The wind whipped at her skirt and blew her hair across her face as Damon put his hand on her shoulder and pointed out the various landmarks to her. She shivered at the contact, but he might have thought it was caused by the sharpness of the wind. He turned her away from her contemplation of the grass-covered crater of the mountain and hurried her back to the car.

They crossed the harbour in one of the squat-looking, elderly ferries that plied the North Shore route, and strolled along the beach at Takapuna in wintry sunshine, watching the children making sandcastles along the narrow shore, and a few hardy souls paddling in the cool gentle waves.

On the return trip they leaned over the rail at the stern of the ship, watching the hypnotic effect of the boat's wake washing creamily behind them, feeling the throb of the engines beneath their feet. Intent on the water with its streaks of blue, green and almost inky purple, and the traffic of small boats and yachts with flighty sails in a variety of saucy, bright colours, Rachel didn't realise that Damon was watching her, until she turned and caught his eye.

'Enjoying yourself?' he asked.

'Yes, thank you.' She gave him a quick, nervous smile and turned back to her contemplation of the harbour, but he caught her face in his hand and turned it back to him.

'I'm not some stranger taking you out for a treat,' he reminded her grimly, and dropped a quick, hard kiss on her mouth before he abruptly released her.

Her fingers curled over the broad wooden rail in front of her. He was her husband—legally. But he might as well have been a stranger for all she really knew of him.

They had a snack lunch in a small coffee bar in Queen Street, at the lower end that the pioneer settlers had reclaimed from the sea.

Then they visited the museum in its beautifully kept garden and park setting, and Rachel made Damon smile at her intense fascination with the replica of a pioneer street with its real shops and houses equipped with antique furniture.

By the time they had visited the Maori meeting house and admired the long canoe that lay in front of it on the ground floor, and murmured over the ancient, intricate carving that decorated them both, the atmosphere between them seemed less strained, and Rachel's smiles more spontaneous.

Before they left they strolled into the shop that occupied a corner of the foyer. Amid the postcards, the multi-coloured paua-shell ornaments and the sketches of native birds and trees, Rachel was admiring a greenstone pendant on a silver chain when Damon came up behind her, asking, 'Do you like it?'

'It's beautiful.' She reluctantly let the pendant drop on its black velvet mounting and turned to go away.

But Damon picked it up and handed it to an assistant and paid for it over her whispered protest.

He didn't give her the small package when it was wrapped, but slipped it into his pocket and then took her arm and led her from the shop.

He told her they were going to dine out, but took her home to change first.

She didn't know what to wear, and when she tentatively voiced her uncertainty he said, 'Wear your wedding dress. Anything goes these days, but it's perfectly suitable.'

She didn't want to, but she was reluctant to go against his wishes and possibly spoil the wary truce they seemed to have established.

When she emerged in the white dress, her hair brushed and shining around her shoulders, Damon was waiting for her, with a glass in his hand. He put it down and came over to her, taking the greenstone pendant from his pocket. He had unwrapped it, and it gleamed softly in his hand.

'This will make it less bridal-looking,' he said, and his hands pushed aside her hair as he clasped the chain about her neck, fumbling a little so that she could feel the warmth of his fingers against her skin for seconds before he dropped his hands.

He didn't move away, but still stood close to her, his grey eyes penetrating. 'Your wedding present,' he said.

'There is an appropriate way to thank me for it—but I'll wait until later.'

There was dancing at the restaurant where he took her, and between courses they joined the other couples on the small, gleaming floor. His hold was firm and close but not intimate when they danced, and he talked to her easily, almost like the man she had known in the summer when they had become friends. When she refused a second glass of wine with her meal he smiled quite kindly and said mildly, 'Perhaps you're right. Last time it sent you to sleep.'

Last time had been only yesterday, but it seemed an age ago. A shadow crossed her face, and he put a hand over hers on the table and said, 'Don't worry, Rachel. You've plenty of time to get used to—new experiences.'

He didn't mean just the wine, and with a return of defiance she moved her fingers sharply from his hold. He regarded her enigmatically for a moment and then poured himself some more wine. His expression had become remote and cool, and she suppressed a pang of regret for her action.

They hardly spoke on the drive back to his home, but Rachel felt herself becoming tense as they neared it. She got out of the car quickly when they arrived, but had to wait for him to open the door with his key.

When she went in ahead of him and began to make for the spare room where she had slept the night before, he caught at her hand, bringing her to a halt.

She looked up at his face, seeing a questioning look there, with a hint of determination about the mouth.

'Thank you, Damon, for today,' she said. 'I enjoyed it.'

He didn't say anything, but drew her closer, his hand tugging on hers, his other arm going round her.

She made a slight movement of dissent, straining away from him, but his hold tightened and he said softly, 'No, you don't, my prudish little *wife*. I'm going to have my thank-you.'

His eyes glittered with determination and something else as he tugged at her hair, raising her reluctant face to his.

His mouth had great firmness and assurance on hers, questing, probing for a response from her. A warm quivering began in the pit of her stomach and spread over her body and she clenched her teeth and tightened all her muscles in an effort to deny it, to stop herself betraying her feelings to him.

He let her go and she almost staggered with reaction and relief. She turned and fled blindly into the bedroom, closing the door and leaning on it to take a few deep, gulping breaths, as though she had been deprived of air.

Long after she had used the bathroom and got into bed, the sliver of light from the living room showed beneath her door. She lay looking at it, tensed as she listened for any sound from Damon. But none came, and eventually she was overcome by sleep.

CHAPTER TWELVE

A FEW days later Damon took her to see Carl Watkins. He was not at all her idea of a publisher's editor, which species she had vaguely imagined as hard-bitten, sophisticated and intimidating.

If she was nervous at the beginning of their meeting, that was soon dispelled. Carl was middle-aged with receding, untidy brown curls, a creased shirt and a suit that in some indefinable way just missed fitting him. His soft brown eyes took her in at a glance with unmistakable kindness, and his delight at meeting Damon's wife was completely genuine.

'Secretive beggar, isn't he?' he asked without animosity. 'Keeping us all in the dark. Well, you'll have your work cut out controlling him, you know.'

He was joking, but as Rachel murmured something about not making the attempt, and smiled back at Carl, she wondered if everyone also knew that Paula had been living with Damon, right up until his marriage. He moved in the sort of circles where that kind of thing was taken for granted, she supposed. The thought was humiliating, and when Damon took her hand and added some joking remark of his own, pulling her to his side, her arm stiffened, and she felt his fingers tighten until they hurt. She supposed he wanted to put up a good front before his friend, and a flash of resentment shot through her, but she had been brought up not to make scenes, and to keep private disagreements private, so she said nothing, only smiling blindly up at Damon in what she hoped was a passable imitation of wifely adoration.

When they began to talk about publishing her poems, she forgot both her resentment and her shyness and by the time they left Carl's office she was excited enough not to scarcely notice Damon's arm about her waist as he steered her towards a nearby park.

They sat down on a green wooden bench, and he put his arm along the back of it, smiling down at her in the old way.

'Pleased with yourself?' he asked.

'Terribly. Is that vain of me?'

'Very. Wait until you see your book in print. You'll be insufferable.'

'Will I?'

'No,' he said softly, and bent to drop a light kiss on her lips.

Her eyes suddenly prickled with tears, and he said abruptly, 'You're over-excited. Stay here and I'll go and get us something to eat.'

He strode off, and the tears disappeared as she watched his straight back go down the tree-lined path. He was fond of her, and perhaps she should build on that, hoping he would come to really care in time, as deeply as she did. Build towers to the sun, from her shattered world of love.

When he came back, with paper bags full of club sandwiches, hot pies and cakes, and two cans of soft drink, she asked lightly, 'Were *you* insufferable, when you saw your first book in print?'

He frowned down at the club sandwich in his hand, and said curtly, 'Apparently.'

Rachel remembered that he had said his girl-friend—his lover—had walked out after reading the book, and biting fiercely into her pie, so that the dark gravy burnt her tongue and dribbled on to her wrist, she wondered how many girl-friends he had made love to since then. Was Paula just the latest in a lengthy line? And had he really loved any of them?

Whatever he had felt for Paula, it had evidently died now. Was that his way with women? A flare of passion, a certain fondness, then— nothing? Off with the old love and on with the new, Paula had said mockingly. And when Rachel became the old love, what then? Would he have found another new one?

She had finished her pie without tasting it, and Damon offered her a sandwich. She took it and watched his long, strong fingers crumple the empty bag before he tossed it in a nearby rubbish bin, and something inside her contracted with love and pain.

He had married her, after all—she recalled how he had reminded her of the words of the marriage ceremony, his insistence that she stay with him, even if their marriage was no more than a farce.

But even then he had called her a child. He thought her too young even though he desired her. He had married her on impulse, perhaps partly because of that desire which sometimes overrode his common sense, but mostly, she was humiliatingly convinced, out of pity.

'Cake?' Damon asked, offering her another bag.

Rachel shook her head, and he remarked, 'You're looking very pensive.'

She didn't answer, and he took a small cake from the bag but instead of eating it, he began to break off bits and feed them to a couple of pigeons hopefully pecking around their feet. The crumbs brought others, and soon a swarm of pigeons and sparrows warbled and fluttered around them.

'Are you going to give them all of it?' Rachel asked as Damon continued pulling the cake into pieces.

'Why not?' he shrugged, his eyes holding hers. 'Since you don't want it?'

She looked away, watching the greedy birds enjoying their treat, and told herself she must stop seeing hidden meanings in everything Damon said and did. If they were to live together it must be on the surface. Digging for deeper emotions would make the whole situation impossible.

A cloud covered the pale sun, and Damon dusted the last crumbs from his fingers and fired the crumbled bag accurately into the rubbish bin. 'Ready to go?' he asked.

She was, but she didn't know where they were going until he steered her into 246 in Queen Street and as they took the escalator upwards, she asked, 'Where are we going?'

'To buy you some clothes.'

The escalator blurred under her downbent gaze, and he grabbed her arm as she tripped at the top, not remembering to lift her feet.

As soon as she was steady on her feet she pulled away from him with a jerk, feeling the heat in her cheeks, her eyes stinging with enraged tears.

'What the hell is the matter now?' Damon asked softly, a hard hand on her back pushing her into a quiet corner away from the stream of hurrying shoppers.

'Why, nothing!' she said with a slightly hysterical little laugh, her eyes burning up at him. 'But I didn't suspect you of such unoriginal thinking, Damon!'

Frowning, he said, 'What's that supposed to mean?'

'It's a bit hackneyed, isn't it?' she said bitterly, trying to smile. 'The rich husband taking his country mouse wife out to buy clothes suitable for his life-style. I'm sorry my clothes are not up to your standards, Damon. Perhaps you should ask Paula to advise me. She's—exquisite.'

He said nothing, but the fury in his face was enough to make her cringe inwardly. He took her arm in a grip that felt hard enough to cut off circulation entirely, and steered her down again to the ground floor without a word, and into the street where she was almost forced into a run to keep up with his long, angry strides until he seemed to notice and slowed down a little. But the grim look about his mouth didn't abate, and it stayed there after they got into the car and all the way back to the house.

Rachel's arm felt bruised where he had gripped her, and she automatically moved her hand to surreptitiously rub it, but he flicked a glance at her and she dropped her hand back on to the handbag she was clutching in her lap.

She walked into the house feeling as though she was going to the block. As Damon closed the door behind them with a controlled little slam, she made across the carpet towards her bedroom, slipping off her jacket.

'Come here!' said Damon, his voice as sharp as whip-crack.

She stopped with her back to him and said stubbornly,

'I want to go to my room.'

'You do and I'll be right behind you.' He spoke softly, but she knew he meant every word.

She turned slowly to face him and tilted her head to a defiant angle, hiding the curling of fear inside her. 'I didn't promise to *obey* you, Damon. Are you going to be a very Victorian husband?'

'You promised a lot of things,' he said. 'Which you don't intend to carry out, apparently. Shall I remind you of some of them?'

She physically recoiled before the cold glitter in his eyes, taking an involuntary step away from him. He must have thought she was going to defy him, and he crossed the room in swift strides and pulled the jacket and bag from her fingers, flinging them aside before he grasped her shoulders and thrust her into the nearest armchair with considerable force.

He stood in front of her, thrusting his hands into his trouser pockets, presumably to keep them off her, she thought. It was hard to make herself meet his eyes, but she was determined not to be intimidated.

'Now,' he said, with cold anger, 'you just sit there and you damn well *listen*. I'm not ashamed of you or of your clothes. I don't give a damn what you wear. I thought we'd buy something for you from one of the supposedly exclusive and best places in town because you seemed to be depressed and I wanted to give you a treat—a present. I've seen you looking sideways into shop windows. It doesn't matter to me if you wear a sackcloth, but you obviously like nice things, like most women, and like most new husbands——' his mouth moved into a bitter little smile, '—I liked the idea of buying something pretty for you.'

Rachel looked away from the smile, because it hurt her, and his voice went on over her head, giving her the impression that he had leaned a little closer to give emphasis to his softly spoken but warning tone. 'And don't you ever throw Paula's name in my face again. I've offered twice to explain—I'm not offering any more. Believe what you like —you'll just have to learn to live with it.'

She looked up then, with a question on the tip of her tongue—*was* there any other explanation than the obvious one? But he had turned away and was striding towards the door.

She watched him as he opened it and went out of the flat, her throat moving to call him back, but her lips would not open.

She sat in the chair for ages, until her limbs felt cramped and she began to shiver with cold. She got up then and switched on the heating system and turned up the thermostat, but it was a long time before she stopped shivering.

When it began to get dark she made herself go into the kitchen and scramble a couple of eggs, but she could only eat half of the meal, and threw the rest away. After clearing up she wandered back to the living room and switched on the TV, but the flickering picture on the screen hardly registered. Was Damon planning to stay away all night? she wondered. Where had he gone?

A picture of a car smash and people on stretchers being carried to an ambulance impinged on her consciousness, and she was suddenly cold with fear. What if he had met with an accident? He had walked out in anger—just the sort of mood in which he might have been likely to be careless and lacking in concentration.

Suddenly flooded with remorse, she thought of his final words to her—*you'll just have to learn to live with it*—and wondered in a panic of fear if she could live with the knowledge that he had died with bitterness between them. He was her husband, after all, and she had taken him for better or worse.

Then the picture on the screen changed, and as she idly watched the characters in a play move across the screen, something vaguely familiar about one of them caught her eye. The woman had long dark hair and was leaning against a door-jamb in a provocative pose, a thin wrapper pulled taut across her breasts. Rachel was reminded of Paula, reclining on Damon's sofa in a similar robe, and for the first time it occurred to her that Damon was with Paula.

She tried to thrust down the worm of suspicion, but it refused to be quieted. There was a man on the screen now with the woman, leaning close to her, his dark head bending to kiss her, and as her pale hands caressed his shoulders, Rachel imagined Paula's hands on Damon. They would be familiar to him—her hands, her mouth, her body——

Rachel got up and snapped the TV off. She was being ridiculous, she told herself. Damon had spoken the other night as though he hated Paula, and he had practically thrown her out of the flat.

But he had been angry then, angry and embarrassed, she supposed. Rachel, too, had been the recipient of his chilly anger this afternoon, and yet it seemed he still wanted her to be his wife.

But where *was* he?

Anxiety began to gnaw again, mixed with anger. He had no right to walk out on her like that, without telling her where he was going, or when he would be back.

She had a long, leisurely bath, which failed completely to calm her taut nerves, and got into one of the seductive nightgowns Anne had helped her choose for her 'trousseau' and pulled over it the matching negligee. It had too much lace on it, but it covered her adequately and hid the provocative nightgown. She wished she had brought some of her old cotton nighties and the reliable quilted nylon brunch coat she had worn back home at the Langholms'. Her father had not minded her sleeping in her skin, but Anne had insisted on nightwear of suitable modesty. But it was apparently permissible for a bride to be somewhat less modest.

Sudden homesickness hit her like a wave, and she choked back tears, not wanting to give way to misery.

The sofa looked inviting, but she didn't want Damon to find her there when he came in, like some pale imitation of Paula. She left the side lights on in the living room and took a book from one of the shelves near Damon's desk in the corner and lay on her bed, with the door firmly shut.

It was after midnight before she finally heard Damon come in. Twice she had switched off her bedside light and tried to sleep. But sleep would not come and she had given up and returned to the book. It was one of Damon's own, a later and, she thought, better novel than *Bread of Deceit*. In spite of her anxious tension, she found, herself caught up in the story and its characters, until the sounds in the living room penetrated her consciousness.

Rachel closed the book and turned off the light, but in her haste the book dropped to the floor with a thwacking thud.

The sounds in the next room ceased, and the next moment her door was flung open, and she blinked as Damon switched on the overhead light.

He looked darkly handsome, tieless and without his jacket, which she glimpsed thrown down on the sofa behind him. He also looked in the peak of health, and all her anxious musings and furious suspicions exploded inside her as she sat up and heard, appalled, her own voice saying sharply, '*Where have you been?*'

For a moment he stayed framed in the doorway; then he stepped into the room and as if it was in slow motion she saw him deliberately close the door and lean against it, his arms folded across his chest, his face grimly mocking.

'What a very wifely greeting,' he drawled. His eyes flickered over the bridal-looking negligee with its lace ruffles, and his eyebrows rose a fraction. 'Have you been practising for the role?'

'I don't know what you're talking about.' Her voice threatened to waver, and the effort to stop it made her sound slightly shrill.

He moved away from the door and strolled over to the bed, flicking the lace that foamed across her breasts with his finger. 'This very fetching little bit of fluff and frills,' he observed. 'It looks—enticing.'

'It's all I have,' she said. 'At least, the others are just as——'

'Seductive?'

'I wasn't to know you would come barging into my room without even knocking!' she flashed. 'You flatter yourself if you think I put this on for *your* benefit.'

He moved, putting his hands flat on the bed on either

side of her so that she was trapped against the pillows.

'I have as much right to come into your room as you do to demand to know where I've been, Rachel,' he said. 'If you're going to assume the prerogatives of a wife——'

He paused, and she said, 'I have to accept the duties, too?'

His mouth straightened and his eyes were flint-hard as he looked down at her. 'You have a very old-fashioned view of marriage, don't you? Most women these days regard the sexual side of it as a pleasure, not a duty.'

'Only where there's love——' she said, staring up at him.

She wouldn't have thought his face could become any more hard and angry than it was, but it did. 'I told you once before,' he said, 'love doesn't always have a lot to do with it.'

He sat on the bed and pulled her up into his arms, pinioning one of hers and holding the other with his hand. Her head fell back and he kissed her, at first fiercely, and then with a deliberate expertise that made her grit her teeth in the effort not to respond.

She tried to struggle, to move her head away from his insistent mouth, but he pushed her back against the bed and held her still while he continued to kiss her, waking emotions which she tried vainly to hide. Her breathing quickened and she trembled faintly under his hands.

She stopped struggling and concentrated on fighting her own impulse to kiss him back. His lips left hers briefly to whisper against her cheek, 'Let go, darling—don't fight me any more.'

She felt an overwhelming urge to succumb as his mouth returned to hers again and began a slow, insistent seduction. His hands lost their hard restraining quality and became persuasively caressing on her shoulders, her throat, and her body. Her own hands clenched at her sides, pressing into the mattress, then feebly tried to push against his shoulders before she let them fall back again, defeated.

She wanted a chance to think—she wanted him to stop her thinking altogether—her confused thoughts battled tiredly with the urgent needs of her body, and she thought, *if only he would say he loves me!*

She moved her head in a tiny, mute protest, and he lifted his mouth from hers and began kissing the hollow at the base of her throat while his fingers pulled at the ribbons that fastened the front of her wrap, and when the edges fell open his mouth seared a path down to the indentation between her breasts that was left bare by the deep neckline of the nightgown.

Her hands moved convulsively and touched his hair. There was a strong temptation to press his dark head closer, but she resisted it and moved her hands to his hard, tautened cheeks, pulling him away.

He moved so that he was on the bed, lying almost fully on her, looking down with glittering eyes into her face, and before he could claim her mouth again, she said urgently, *'Damon!'*

He paused, and she put her hands against his chest, holding him off. 'Damon, why did you marry me?'

'Why? You little fool, why do you think?' Impatiently, he lowered his head to hers again, but she shied away, turning her lips from him and beginning to struggle again in his arms.

He grasped her hair and pulled her head back, making her face him. His eyes were on her mouth and she said frantically, 'Damon! Damon—please answer me!'

He didn't lift his gaze to her pleading eyes, but muttered deeply, 'Isn't this answer enough for you?' and kissed her again, his mouth hard on hers with hungry passion.

She had her answer, and it was bitter. Desire—not love. She felt that something inside her had gone cold and shrivelled, and the desire he had aroused ebbed even as his lips and hands became more compelling. His mouth hurt her and his hands felt brutal on her shrinking skin as they impatiently pulled aside the silky folds of the flimsy nightwear that had been bought in expectation of love and consideration, and some tenderness. She thought of Des and his callousness.

Eventually her frozen stillness got through to him, and he paused, one hand shaping her bared shoulder, and the other heavily on her hip, his thumb stilled where it had been stroking the softness of smooth flesh that covered the narrow bone.

Flatly, he said, 'You're not pretending, are you? You really are hating this.'

Bitterly, out of her pain, she retorted, 'Is that so hard to believe? Are you such a Great Lover?'

'Apparently not.' He rolled off the bed and stood up, looking at her dishevelled state of half-undress with cynical eyes. 'But the lady is usually more—co-operative.'

She thought he meant *experienced,* and flinched at the implied criticism.

'Don't worry,' he said, flicking up the bed cover from where it lay rumpled at the foot of bed, and throwing it carelessly across her, 'I won't bother you again.' He laid a slight stress on the '*you*,' and as he pulled the door to behind him with a decisive but controlled slam, Rachel wondered miserably if he meant he would be going to some other woman for what she could not give him. Or *would* not. She wondered if she had been less inexperienced if she might have been able to make love with him regardless of the depth of his feeling for her. She supposed the co-operative ladies that he mentioned hadn't been too bothered about deep and lasting feelings. But they had not been married to him.

That brought her back to her growing and chilling conviction that what he had wanted from her had been exactly the same as what he had wanted from them—but he had married her because her youth and inexperience had made him feel guilty for wanting her, and the legality of the licence eased the guilt.

CHAPTER THIRTEEN

SPRING in the city came subtly, Rachel discovered. Some of the streets were lined with plane trees that began showing tiny buds of green and then seemed suddenly showered with leaves that hid the grey knobbly deformity of their severely pruned branches. Fruit trees bloomed in gardens and manuka that had been domesticated and specially bred to produce spectacular bloom in every shade of pink or red burst into unbelievable blossom, twiggy branches heavily covered in flowers up to an inch wide, that put their modest wild cousins to shame.

Daisies grew in the tiny lawn behind the house and she was able to buy outdoor mushrooms that reminded her of Hawkes Bay and the station. The spring grass would be lush and soft and the lambs would be grazing the lower slopes with their mothers, small tails busily wagging as they butted at the ewes for their milk.

She cooked the mushrooms for Damon after enquiring if he liked them, and receiving his courteous assurance that he did. He was always very polite to her these days, a polite, urbane stranger who lived in the same house, on the other side of an invisible glass barrier that was always between them, that allowed them to converse and sometimes even laugh together, but which neither of them ever tried to break down.

He had not touched her since the night he had come home late and found her waiting for him. Not so much as a fingertip had he laid on her, for any reason whatsoever, in nearly two months.

Rachel had exerted herself to remember all Anne's training and become a superb cook and housekeeper. She had asked Damon to stop employing the woman who used to

THE JASMINE BRIDE 155

clean for him, and he had given her a thoughtful look and
agreed. Not for anything would she have admitted that it
was not only because she felt the need to occupy her time,
but also because she was embarrassed to think that the
woman would inevitably guess that they were not sharing a
room.

And buried deep in her subconscious was another, barely
acknowledged thought, that she could somehow make up to
Damon for not being his wife in the fullest sense, by ex-
celling in other spheres.

Damon accepted her efforts with apparent tolerance, but
she often caught a faint trace of derision in his face as he
watched her serve a meal or arrange a vase of flowers on one
of the tables in the living room.

She entertained his friends once or twice to dinner, and
he thanked her meticulously afterwards, complimenting
her on her cooking. They were invited out, too, and no one
seemed to notice the lack of physical contact between them,
even though they teased Damon about his sudden and
secret marriage. His sister challenged him about it, laugh-
ingly.

'It wasn't secret,' Damon answered easily. 'Nor even so
sudden, really. We'd known each other for months, and
once we decided to get married, there was no reason for
delay, that's all. Rachel has no people and we both wanted
a minimum of fuss—isn't that right, darling?'

He smilingly lifted his glass to her across the space that
separated their chairs in his sister's lounge, and Rachel
smiled back and said, 'That's right. *I* didn't want to wait
an extra day, let alone two weeks!'

Her eyes challenged him, and though his smile stayed on
his face, she saw the way his knuckles tensed as the hand
holding his glass tightened, and was glad that she had
pricked him a little. She knew he had told his sister about
her before the wedding, but not invited her to attend.

They were nice, Frances and her husband, and Frances
didn't have her brother's streak of occasional ruthless
mockery. Rachel would have enjoyed the evening if she had
not been constantly on guard against any slip that would

betray that things were not entirely normal between herself and her husband.

She was surprised when Damon said, on their way home, 'Thank you, Rachel.'

'What for?' She searched his face for signs of mockery, but he looked quite grave.

'For pretending.' His voice had hardened a little, but he didn't look at her.

She couldn't pretend not to know what he meant, but no reply was possible. She looked out into the darkness in silence.

'Did you like them?' he asked abruptly, after a while.

'Very much. Your sister isn't much like you.'

'Thanks!'

She turned to him quickly, saying, 'I didn't mean it like that! You mustn't—mistake everything I say.'

'Do I? Did I mistake the accusing look when you reminded me it wasn't your idea to wait two weeks for our marriage? I confess I didn't understand it, but the message seemed clear enough.'

Evading the issue, she said, 'It was true.'

Damon made an exasperated sound and turned his attention wholly to the road for the rest of the drive.

Rachel was in Auckland city one day when she saw the face of Paula Winfield in a photograph outside a theatre. The shock brought her up short for a moment before she hurried on down the street, and it was some time before she realised she had passed the shop she had been going to, and slowly retraced her steps. So Paula was an actress!

From then on, Paula seemed to haunt her. She opened a magazine and saw a smaller photograph and the information that a television casting director had seen her stage performance and snapped her up for a leading role in a home-grown drama for television.

She picked up a Sunday paper and there was an article in it about Paula, described as the 'hottest talent on the New Zealand entertainment scene at present.' Compulsively, she read the accompanying interview, in which Paula came across as a sharp-witted, interesting personality, but also as a hard worker who was only now beginning to reap the benefits of many years of dedicated work. There was also a hint that a 'long-standing relationship' had interrupted her career for a time, but that Paula had eventually become bored with the affair and was now determined to advance her career.

Rachel tried hard to forget the date scheduled for screening of the television play, but it seemed indelibly engraved on her mind, and when Damon announced that evening that he was going out, as he quite often did, she fatalistically turned the TV on at the appropriate time and watched it, even as she castigated herself for unhealthy masochism.

Paula's performance was undoubtedly good, so much that at times Rachel felt herself believing in the character on the screen, and almost forgetting her personal involvement with the woman who played it.

Afterwards she sat through an inferior comedy and the late news, hardly taking them in, but loth to switch off and plunge the flat into silence. When Damon was out it always seemed very empty, although there was a certain relief in the easing of tension.

He came in late, and she had been in bed with the light out for some time. She never asked where he had been when he went out, but she couldn't sleep until she heard him come in. She looked more heavy-eyed after his late forays than he did.

Her nineteenth birthday was coming up, and she wondered if Damon would remember it. When he told her they had been invited to a party on that date, she thought he had not, until he added, 'Shall we go out to dinner first? To celebrate your birthday. It won't matter if we arrive a little late at the party.'

'That would be nice,' she said carefully. 'I didn't think you would remember.'

'How could I forget?' he drawled rather sardonically, and she thought that his eyes were on her mouth. She remembered her last birthday, when he had held her close and

kissed her and been gentle with her. She recalled the softness of the night air and the scent of jasmine that had
lingered on her hands after he left her.

She dressed with care on the evening of her birthday.
Damon had been out most of the day, something to do with
the promotion for his recent book, she gathered. He was
working on another, but he never talked about it, and she
didn't dare investigate the folders on his desk in the corner
of the sitting room, where he slipped each page as he
finished it.

He came in late, but was ready before she was, and
when she emerged from her room his glance over her simple
sea-green chiffon gown which bared most of her shoulders
and lightly emphasised the sweet curves of her young figure
was comprehensive but almost impersonal.

He picked up a small package from the table beside him
and came towards her. Rachel had clasped the jade pendant
he had given her about her throat, but he put the package
in her hands and reached up to unfasten the chain. The un-
familiar touch of his fingers made her shiver.

'Now open it,' he said, stepping back.

She slowly stripped off the paper and opened the box
inside, revealing a small, pink-tinted teardrop pearl in a
delicate filigree setting on a silver chain.

'Put it on,' he said, and she fumbled as she did so, but
he didn't attempt to help.

When her hands dropped, Damon stood looking at the
necklace for a long moment, then he put a hand on her
waist and steered her to her bedroom, and made her stand
in front of the dressing table mirror.

'Like it?' he asked.

Rachel couldn't read the expression on his face, reflected
behind her shoulder in the mirror. She touched the pearl,
and it trembled under her fingertips. 'It's beautiful,' she
said. 'It's real, isn't it?'

'Of course.'

'Thank you, Damon.'

His eyes changed, and he looked faintly challenging. She

thought he moved a little back, and she turned to move away, but he was still standing very close, looking down into her eyes with a question unmistakably in his.

She swallowed nervously and put a hand on his shoulder, raising herself against him to kiss the corner of his mouth. He seemed to be holding himself quite rigid, and he made no move to meet the kiss or to return it.

When she stepped back, confused, he said, 'Pearls suit you. They belong to the sea, too.'

Perhaps it was the exquisite food, or the wine that Damon persuaded her to have, or perhaps he was consciously exerting himself to make her birthday happy, but over their dinner, there seemed very little tension. Rachel enjoyed herself, talking freely with her husband between courses, and finding him almost the stimulating but easy companion that he had been when they had swum together and explored the rock pools in the little bay that she thought of as home.

By the time they moved on to the party, it seemed natural that he should put his arm about her as they entered the house, that he keep it there as their hostess introduced them to the guests they didn't know.

Some of them Rachel already knew slightly. She was glad to see Carl Watkins and his wife among them. She had met Carl several times now, and liked him very much. She had also been to his house and met his wife and three teen-age children.

'Shouldn't be talking business,' said Carl, winking at her, 'but your book will definitely be out by Christmas.'

The news seemed to set the seal on the evening, and Rachel sparkled and lost most of her shyness, enjoying the convivial atmosphere, her appreciation heightened by Damon's lightly possessive hold on her shoulder as they sat side by side on a sofa. Usually he managed to sit slightly away from her, so that they didn't come into physical contact.

It was nearing midnight when Damon referred casually to it being Rachel's birthday, and Carl hailed their host and informed him of the fact.

Before Rachel could protest the whole room had joined in singing Happy Birthday to her and drinking a rousing toast. She laughed and flushed with pleased embarrassment, and then into the silence which followed, a light unmistakable voice said from the doorway of the room, 'Sorry I'm so late, dears—but I couldn't get away until after the show, and all the taxi drivers seem to have gone home!'

'Paula!' Their hostess went towards the latecomer and embraced her, drawing her into the room, as all heads turned to watch—and appreciate—Paula Winfield, looking glamorous and extremely beautiful in a low-cut, clinging dress of some glittery, thin synthetic.

'And who's having a birthday?' she asked, gliding across the floor in her hostess's wake, with infinite grace.

'Damon's wife,' the other woman replied, and steered her towards Damon and Rachel who were standing close together, Rachel frozen as still as a marble statue, and Damon's fingers on her arm tightened painfully, though she scarcely noticed. 'You two won't have met——'

'Oh, but we have——' Paula told her, and Rachel almost flinched as the actress fleetingly kissed her suddenly cold cheek. 'Happy birthday, dear. How old are you?'

'Nineteen,' Rachel responded automatically, dimly relieved that the hum of conversation about them had begun again. She wondered how many of them knew about Damon and Paula, and supposed she should be grateful for their tact.

'Nineteen!' Paula repeated, her eyebrows delicately rising. 'Really, Damon!' she said, mockingly chiding, and glancing at him, Rachel saw a faint flush rise under his tan. Returning her eyes to Rachel, Paula said soothingly, 'I mustn't tease, though. You do make a very sweet child bride.'

To Rachel's relief, someone plucked at Paula's arm and drew her away. She stood feeling young and somehow diminished, all her confidence in her own appearance overshadowed by Paula's sophisticated, mature poise. Her growing hope that Damon did, or could truly love her, that she could make him hers if only she was generous enough to forget the past and willing to take second best for a while, was suddenly and completely dashed. How could she ever compete with someone as desirable, as practised, as altogether lovely and talented and clever as Paula?

'Let's get some air,' Damon said in her ear, and steered her rapidly across the room to where a pair of ranchslider doors opened on to a wide patio, where a few couples danced in the dim light to the music of a portable record-player.

He put his arms around her and pulled her close to him and began to move to the music. Automatically she followed his steps, but her muscles refused to relax against the movements of his. His hands began to gently caress her back, and his mouth brushed her temple.

'Loosen up, for heaven's sake,' he murmured. 'You're as stiff as a poker.'

She tried, and his hands tightened on her, fitting her closely to his body, telling her without words that he liked the feel of her against him.

The music stopped, and he lifted a hand to the back of her neck and pressed a brief, sensuous kiss on her lips, before his hold on her loosened a little. She half-turned away from him, and saw Paula framed in the lighted doorway with a man. Her heart thudded as she wondered if the kiss had been for Paula's benefit. Sickly, it occurred to her that Damon might have known Paula would be at the party tonight, that his unusual attentions to herself had been aimed at presenting to the other woman a picture of wedded bliss—to make her jealous? Or to show her that their affair was over? Perhaps simply to salve his pride, by pretending that he had not, after all, made a ghastly mistake.

Someone had changed the record, and Damon drew her back into his arms, but in her misery she didn't follow well, and twice she stumbled and missed the beat.

'What's the matter?' he asked, and she wondered if the irritability in his voice was real or a figment of her own imagination.

'I'm tired,' she said. 'Could we go home soon?'

For a moment he didn't answer. Then he said, 'Soon. If that's what you want. But not just yet . . .'

When the music paused, he pushed her down on a wooden corner seat in the shadows, and said, 'I'll get you a drink. Perhaps it will help.'

He disappeared inside before she could protest, and she sat feeling jaded and wrung out, dejectedly saying to herself, *where do we go from here*? Dimly she knew that she and Damon could not go on living as they were now. It was unnatural, and too much of a strain.

She dropped her head into her hands, smoothing her fingers over a forehead that was beginning to ache.

A light, clear voice made her look up, startled. 'Do you smoke, Rachel?' A slender white hand proffered a pack of cigarettes.

Rachel shook her head, then realising that Paula could scarcely see her in the dark corner, said stiffly, 'No, thank you.'

Paula sat down on the other half of the seat, at right angles to Rachel's, lit a cigarette and leaned back, one arm spread along the back of the seat, and blew smoke elegantly into the night air.

'How are you getting along with Damon?' she asked negligently.

'All right,' Rachel lied stiffly.

Paula made a small grimace. 'I suppose that's not a question to put to a new bride,' she said. 'But you're very young, and Damon can be a difficult cuss when he likes.' She drew a quick breath on her cigarette and added abruptly, 'I'm sorry if I loused up that first night.'

Rachel sat in stony silence, her nails curling into the palms of her hands as she clenched them in her lap.

Paula gave a soft, rueful laugh. 'I'm not doing this very well, honey, but I'm trying to apologise. I behaved rather badly that night, I'm afraid, in more ways than one. I frequently do—with Damon. He always had a knack of getting under my skin, one way or another.' She paused, took another long draw on her cigarette, and said, 'Of course, you know what I was—hoping for, that night, waiting for Damon.'

'You hoped to take up where you had left off,' Rachel said in a small, clear voice.

Paula cast her a sharp glance, and said, 'Well, you could put it like that. Of course, it went horribly wrong—I had no idea about *you*. Look—I don't remember everything I said, but I'm not a nice person when I'm feeling—humiliated. Of course, I took it out on Damon. He can take it, but I've nothing against you, and you seem a nice kid—what I'm trying to say is, Damon hasn't cared for me for a long time. So you don't need to worry. The embers I was trying to stir up were long dead.' Even in the darkness Rachel could see a hint of her wry smile. 'I hope you believed him when he told you that.'

He hadn't told her that. He had told her nothing, but pride kept Rachel silent. She wondered how long a 'long time' was in Paula's language—or Damon's. Their codes of behaviour were different from hers.

Damon's hard voice interrupted them. 'Hallo, Paula. Stirring up trouble?'

'How suspicious you are, Damon!' she drawled, stubbing out her cigarette. 'Actually I was pouring a little oil, that's all. I like your wife, Damon. You don't deserve her.'

He stared hard at her pale face upturned in the darkness and said shortly, 'I know it.' Then he handed the glass in his hand to Rachel and said, 'Drink up.'

She didn't even taste it as she obeyed, glad to have something to do.

Paula stood up and said, 'Dance with me, Damon—you don't mind, do you, Rachel?'

She didn't wait for Rachel to answer, but moved closer to Damon, linking her hands about his neck, and after a moment he lifted his to rest on her waist, and they moved away into the flow of couples swaying across the patio.

They were not dancing any closer to each other than any other couple, but their bodies seemed finely attuned, as though they had been through the motions many times before. Rachel could see their faces in the light that was shed from inside, and she watched as Paula's head went back as she talked, and Damon's face changed gradually from grim suspicion to a softer, even amused visage. When the number stopped, they stayed in each other's arms, and Rachel saw Paula's hands move up to the dark hair above Damon's collar and then come round to rest their fingertips against his cheekbones. And Damon smiled.

He put up his own hand and caught one of Paula's, and Rachel recalled how he had kissed hers, once or twice, his beautiful mouth moving on the soft inner skin of her wrist, pressing into her palm. Blindly she turned away and made her way rapidly across the patio into the lighted room.

Smoke and noise seemed to flow out at her in waves, and she almost pushed her way through to the bar where she left her empty glass, before looking round rather desperately for Carl.

She found him ensconced in a corner of the room, and perched herself on the arm of his chair, asking where his wife was.

'Around, somewhere,' he told her, waving vaguely. 'And what about your husband?'

'Around,' she echoed, determinedly gay, copying his gesture and making him laugh.

A dark young man with a moustache came over to them, eyeing Rachel with appreciation and saying, 'Oh, you're the birthday girl—congratulations.'

'You can congratulate her on her marriage too,' Carl growled. 'It's fairly recent. Rachel, this is Brent Conners —don't believe a word he says. No woman is safe when he's around.'

'Slander,' Brent Conners said easily. 'I'm as innocent as a newborn babe.'

His own eyes belied it as they wandered appreciatively over her with a decided gleam in them, and Carl snorted derisively.

Carl was probably right, Rachel thought, but with him sitting right there beside her and in the midst of the party she was perfectly safe, and with the thought of Damon and

Paula still dancing together on the patio in her mind, she listened to and laughed at Brent's flirtatious banter with every appearance of enjoyment. She divided her attention between the two men and successfully managed to stop herself even attempting to peer through the crowd in the room to see if Damon and Paula had come back into it.

It seemed an age before Damon's voice said, 'I've been looking for you, Rachel. I thought you wanted to go home.'

'I thought *you* weren't in any hurry,' she said. She looked smilingly at her two companions. 'I don't mind, but if you want to go——' She shrugged as though reluctant to give up a good time, and Brent laughed and said,

'I don't blame him, Rachel. If you were *my* new wife I'd be in a hurry to get home too.'

Her cheeks warmed, and she didn't resist when Damon grasped her arm and took her with him, bidding the two men a chilling goodnight.

By the time they got to the car she had cooled somewhat. Damon shot out into the street rather fast, and drove at a bare fraction above the speed limit, as though controlling a desire to break the law with a vengeance.

'You seemed to be enjoying yourself with Conners,' he remarked without inflection.

Not reminding him that Carl had been there too, she said coolly, 'I liked him. He was fun.'

'Really?' He turned a swift glance on her, and the slight note of criticism in his voice riled her a little.

'Weren't *you* enjoying yourself?' she asked pointedly. She didn't need to add, *with Paula.* He knew what she meant.

To her surprise, he laughed shortly. 'Were you jealous?'

'*No.* Were you?'

'Yes.'

That silenced her. She shot a glance at his hard profile, but it told her nothing.

They drove on in silence until he asked, 'What did Paula say to you?'

'That she was sorry for what happened the first time we met.'

He didn't move, but she thought he was somewhat surprised.

'Is that all?' he asked.

That you don't care for her any more, she thought. She had thought Paula was being sincere and rather generous. But later she had remembered that the woman was an actress, and apparently an outstanding one. Watching her dance in Damon's arms, she had wondered if the conversation had been designed to allay suspicion. Given Paula's implied opinion of her as a rather naïve child bride who had taken on in Damon more than she could well handle, the suspicion did not seem too fantastic.

'*Is that all?*' Damon reiterated.

'She said that you were difficult to live with,' Rachel admitted.

Damon drew in an audible breath. 'Did she indeed?' he said icily.

Recklessly Rachel went on, 'She seemed to think I might benefit from her experience.'

He was pulling to the curbside, and slowing the car. 'In which direction, in particular?' he asked, turning to her as he cut the engine.

She didn't answer him, sitting very still as though afraid to provoke any movement from him.

'I can think of *one* area in which Paula has a great deal more experience than you,' he said, reaching for her.

She fought him, but it was no contest. In no time he had her firmly imprisoned, one arm holding her against him, and the other hand turning her unwilling face to his, until his mouth crushed the protests from her lips, pressing her head back against the leather of the seat back. He had been drinking whisky, and at first it repelled her and she was glad. But then the scent of his skin reached her, and as he forced her lips to open under his she tasted nothing but the seductive demand of his mouth, making her give up to him the sweetness of hers.

It was a long time before he moved a little away, looking down at her face in the moonlight that streaked through the window. A car purred by, illuminating them momentarily in its headlights, and Rachel made a tentative movement away from him.

Damon didn't let her go immediately, but said, 'Well, you're at least old enough and *married* enough for something more than the bare peck I gave you on your last birthday.'

Then he let her go and started the car.

CHAPTER FOURTEEN

'Six months!' Rachel stared at Damon, who was standing before the window with the letter from America in his hand. With the light behind him it was difficult to gauge the expression on his face.

'Possibly less,' said Damon. 'I've never been a "script adviser" before, but I gather the time period tends to be flexible, depending on how well the filming goes.'

'When will we have to leave?' she asked.

Damon carefully said, 'I'm going alone, Rachel.'

She felt the blood draining from her face, leaving it cold and still. 'But we're married,' she said stupidly.

'Are we?' Damon suddenly threw down the letter—the invitation from the company that had bought the film rights to his book to take on the job of script adviser—on to his desk. Savagely he said, 'It's difficult enough here—how do you think we'd cope over there? For a start, there'd be hotels—they tend to expect married couples to share a room, at least. Do you think we could keep up this—farce —in a place like Hollywood?'

She thought that being thrown together in a different environment might be what they needed to put their marriage on some sort of bearable basis, but when she haltingly tried to say so, he cut her off harshly.

'No! I'm sorry to deprive you of the glamour of a trip to Hollywood, but there are more important considerations. Perhaps a separation might help to—get things into perspective.'

Hurt and stung by the implication that she was only concerned with the idea of glamour, Rachel said tightly, 'And what am I supposed to do for six months?'

'I suggest you enrol at university in the new year, and

commence your studies. If you don't like the idea of staying here on your own, I'm sure Frances will put you up.'

'Thank you, I'll make my own arrangements,' she snapped, furious at the way he was disposing of her in this high-handed fashion.

He said, 'Frances would be pleased to have you.'

'I said I'll make my own arrangements!'

'Rachel, for God's sake, this is difficult enough. I want to be sure you're being looked after——'

'It's all right, I can look after myself.'

He paused, his mouth tight, then said with determined calm, 'You'll be able to draw on our joint account. There'll be plenty of money.'

'Thank you,' she said sarcastically. It was no good—he wasn't going to listen to anything she said. He was walking out of her life with no guarantee that he would ever come back. Suddenly nothing mattered except that he keep her with him. Pride cast to the winds, she moved close to him and pleaded, 'Please, Damon—let me come with you. It could be a new start for us, couldn't it?' She touched his arm, letting her fingers slide up his sleeve to rest on his shoulder. 'I'll share—anything you want—if you just take me with you.'

'Well, well!' he said softly, and the contempt in his face chilled her as her hand dropped away from him. 'I suppose it's true that every woman has her price. And I've just found out what yours is!'

He left on a grey day of gusty winds and light drizzling rain, and Rachel didn't even offer to accompany him to the airport. They no longer had that kind of relationship. They had no relationship at all, she told herself dully as she watched the clock creep round to the flight departure time. They had scarcely spoken to each other since the day he told her he was leaving, and he had been out a good deal, making arrangements, she supposed, for his departure.

Even the publication of her book and the critics' mildly enthusiastic reception of it had failed to more than momentarily dispel the fog of misery that enveloped her. Damon, to give him credit, had tried to inject some real warmth into his congratulations, but her stony reception of his quick kiss and stilted words had put paid to the effort.

They spent a quiet Christmas with his sister and her family, and managed to put a good face on it for the day, but the strain told, and on their return to the flat they parted without even saying goodnight, to go to their separate beds.

There was no doubt that mingled with her numb grief at his departure was a modicum of relief that at last the waiting was over.

She thought of taking his advice and enrolling at university. It would at least give her something to occupy her mind. Poetry seemed to have deserted her, and she could no longer pretend that the house kept her busy all day.

The day she read the news item in the paper about Paula Winfield having left for Hollywood in the hope of breaking into the film industry there, she packed and closed up the flat and took a bus to Hawkes Bay.

She knew from Anne Langholm's letter that Jerry had left the farm and was somewhere in the South Island, deerstalking for a living. It was an unpleasant surprise to find that the farmworker they had hired to replace him was Des Alexander. He looked at her with jeering speculation when they first came face to face, but it was easy to avoid him most of the time, because Anne made little demur about letting her have the old cottage by the sea, and although she visited the homestead quite often, she tried to avoid the times that Des was likely to be about.

Anne and Bert were as kind to her as ever, but she thought they were a little baffled by her wanting to live alone, although accepting her desire for independence. After all, they reasoned, she was a married woman now. They even accepted, with some puzzlement but little comment, her explanation that Damon would find his new job demanding and requiring more concentration than he could give it if she had gone with him. She was well aware that in the Langholms' view a wife's place was with her husband.

She noticed Anne's relief when the letters from America began to arrive, long blue airmail envelopes redirected from the Auckland address. Damon wrote twice a week at first, and later less frequently, and she put them all away in a drawer without opening any of them.

As a sort of compromise, she had enrolled as an extra-mural student with Massey University, which specialised in correspondence lessons. She was used to working that way, and it suited her. But the work left her still plenty of time to swim and lie on the sand and take restless walks. And think.

Probably Damon had known that Paula was going to America. No wonder he had not wanted Rachel along, too. Perhaps his apparent dislike of Paula was genuine, but he had not always disliked her, and he had told Rachel several times that liking and even love had little to do with sexual attraction. She had watched Paula soften him from antagonism to amused tolerance in the space of a few minutes on a dance floor. What would she be able to accomplish in six months? Even if they had made no pre-arrangement, they were bound to meet, two New Zealanders far from home in the glamour of Hollywood.

Looking back, Rachel saw her own mistakes with piercing clarity. Damon, whatever his motives for their marriage, had wanted to make it work, but she had been too hurt to let him explain, too idealistic to accept that what he had to offer her was less than a wholehearted love. She had wanted all or nothing, and what she had was—nothing.

Now it was too late. She was nothing to him but a responsibility and an encumbrance, and an obstacle in the way of his happiness with Paula, perhaps, if the other woman had succeeded in making him care for her again.

Out of her pain she began to write again, starting with a poem which she copied into a fresh notebook under the title, *To D——*, for even though the book was intended for no one's eyes but hers, the outpouring of love and anguish was too personal, and she shied from putting his name in full.

After the first, other poems rapidly filled the book, all on the same theme, all passionately loving, a frank overflowing of emotion that had been pent up too long.

She was writing in her notebook at the kitchen table one day when there was a knock on the outer door, immediately followed by the sound of it opening, and Des Alexander's voice calling her name.

'What do you want?' Rachel demanded as she entered the sitting room. He was standing holding the open door in his hand, but he shut it as he saw her and said, 'Just a social call, Rachel. Haven't seen you for a while.'

'I'm very busy,' she said. 'Don't you have work to do?'

'Not that much. It's slack right now. And Bert and Anne have gone to town for the day. I'm lonely, Rachel.'

She remembered the form that his loneliness took, and tried to be brisk and discouraging without antagonising him. 'I'm not,' she said.

His smile was suggestive. 'Yes, you are. You must be—away from your husband and all.' He moved closer and with an effort she refrained from running. She wouldn't make the back door before he caught her.

'Don't touch me!' she said sharply, but he kept on coming, reaching for her.

'Be nice to me, Rachel,' he said. 'You must be missing it, eh?'

She hit him, and he pulled her wrist behind her, twisting until it hurt. She fought him desperately until she realised that it was exciting him more, that he liked the feeling of power it gave him to subdue her, to hurt. He pushed her down on the sofa and she made herself stop struggling, hoping he would be bored and give up if he found no response and no resistance, or that her lack of fight would make him relax a little so that she could escape while he was off guard.

When his hot mouth found hers she felt sick. She contemplated sinking her teeth into his lip, but was afraid it would make him really violent. He had the edge on her in physical strength. She would have to fight with her intelligence.

Then vaguely she heard the sound outside, and as it

registered in her mind what it was, the door was thrust open and Des lifted his head and struggled up to face the man who stood there.

Pushing tumbled hair out of her eyes, Rachel gasped, faintly unbelieving, 'Damon!'

Des recovered from the shock more quickly than she did. 'Mr Curtis, I presume,' he said insolently. 'Your wife and I were just—talking over old times.'

'Such as?' Damon enquired in a deadly tone.

'Didn't she tell you? We were—friends, Rachel and I. She was very friendly last year—a very kindhearted girl, your wife. Used to come walking with me after tea. We had some good times.'

'That isn't true!' snapped Rachel, catching her breath at last. 'Des—You——'

'Aw, don't say you've forgotten,' Des drawled, casting a mocking glance at her. 'You must remember the time old Jerry caught us behind the woolshed—fit to be tied, he was. He said you were *his* girl—but then you married someone else.' He turned to Damon. 'She's quite a girl, our Rachel. Tell you what, mate, if she was my wife I wouldn't let her out of my sight. She gets lonely quick——'

'*Shut up!*' Damon moved, and Rachel saw Des tense, but Damon only stood by the door, leaving it open for Des to leave. 'Get out,' he said in that deadly quiet tone. 'And if you come near my wife again, I'll take you apart.'

He looked capable of it, and Des sauntered out the door without a word, perhaps aware that he had almost gone too far.

'Oh, Damon!' Rachel said shakily, when he had closed the door. 'I'm so glad you came. He frightened me badly.'

'Did he?' Damon's voice was curiously flat. 'I didn't notice you struggling.'

'I wasn't,' she said. His hard face was chilling, and the explanation she was about to offer died in her throat. He wasn't going to believe her, anyway. 'I wasn't,' she repeated, her voice as expressionless as his own. 'How did you know I was here? Why did you come back? You can't have finished yet.' She struggled to keep the wild hope from her voice, so that it came out toneless and indifferent.

'When I found you weren't at home, I guessed where you would be,' he said. 'The Post Office confirmed it from the redirection order. Which means you've received my letters.' He looked angry and fed up.

'Yes,' she said.

His face seemed to tighten, she felt his teeth were clenched together. 'You haven't answered them,' he said.

'There didn't seem much point in writing,' she said wearily, not telling him she had not read the letters, had not wanted to peruse any polite dutiful notes detailing, no doubt, his travels and the interesting people he met; to read, perhaps, a casual reference to having seen Paula once or twice, or even worse, no reference to her at all in an effort to spare his wife's feelings.

'I'll get my bag,' he said, turning to the door, and she asked,

'You're staying here?'

He turned back to her. 'The Langholms will think it rather strange if I ask to stay with them, won't they, if my *wife* is here? There are two bedrooms.'

Rachel sank down on the sofa and Damon got two bags and hurled them into the spare bedroom, then turned to her and said, 'I could do with a cup of coffee. You look as though you could, too.'

She made to get up, but he said harshly, 'I'll make it. Stay there.'

She thanked him automatically when he brought it, and sipped gratefully at the hot liquid. He had not really told her why he was here, but she didn't dare to ask again.

He drank his coffee standing in front of the window, staring silently at the sea, and took her empty cup from her back to the kitchen. She sat on, feeling curiously drained of all emotion, of life itself. Inertia became lethargy, and she almost dozed, her head falling back on the cushions.

A sudden thought jerked her wide awake, and she jumped to her feet and almost ran to the kitchen doorway, because Damon had not come back, and she had just remembered what she had left on the table.

He was leaning over the table, reading from her notebook, his hand on the open page. He must have had time to read almost all of it now, right from the first poem, dedicated *To D——*.

She lunged across to snatch the book from him, but he saw her coming and snapped it shut, holding it firmly in one hand and grabbing at her wrist with the other as she tried to wrest it from him.

'Who are they for, Rachel?' he asked, a glitter in his grey eyes that frightened her.

'*Myself!*' she said wildly. 'You had no right to read them!'

'You know what I mean,' he said impatiently, ignoring the question of rights altogether. 'Those are love poems, Rachel, every one of them. *Who is he? Des?*'

About to deny it, she swallowed nervously, and he took her shoulders in his hands, dropping the book unheeded on the table beside them, and shook her with brief fierceness. 'Answer me, damn you! Was it true what he said about you? Was that why you weren't fighting him? Because you *wanted* him to make love to you? Because these poems were for *him?*'

'*Don't!*' she protested. 'You can't know what you're saying!' It made so little sense.

'Oh, I know!' he assured her in a hard voice. 'And so did Des, when he told me how *lonely* you've been.'

'You don't—you can't believe him!' She looked at him in horror.

'Can't I? There's plenty of evidence, isn't there? I saw you myself, lying in his arms without a murmur of protest.' His grip changed, his arms going round her body to haul her close to him, one hand sliding up her back to lift her face to him. 'Well, you needn't be lonely any more, darling. Your husband has come back, and if you want a man, I'm happy to oblige.'

His hand was caught in her hair, giving her no chance to evade his kiss, and his mouth was ruthless, simply taking all he could without letting her futile struggles deter him in the least. Her closed lips were pressed against her teeth until they hurt, and she had to obey his unspoken demand to open them. She nipped his lower lip sharply with her teeth, but he pulled her hair fiercely until she let go, and kept on pulling until her head tipped back to let him make a fiery path of kisses down the length of her throat, leaving a faint trail of blood on her smooth skin.

One hand had slipped inside her blouse and was on her bare back, hard and warm, and the other began to pull impatiently at the buttons that stopped his mouth below her collarbone.

Rachel let out a shuddering breath as the buttons gave way, and put up her own hands, trying frantically to stop the exploration that his mouth and hands were making of her body. His hand caught at her wrist and this time the trick of twisting it out and down worked, releasing her arm, and she managed to evade the looser hold of his arm about her waist, and escape from him.

She slammed the kitchen door in his face and flew across the other room, wrenching open the door to run down the path towards the beach. She was half-way to the sand when his shout behind her made her involuntarily glance upward and her flying feet tripped over a tuft of grass, she fell headlong down the slope and hit her head on a protruding rock at the bottom.

She must have been out for a few minutes, and when she became aware again, Damon was carrying her up the path. He took her inside and put her on the bed, and bathed a trickle of blood from her temple. She felt it, and there was a swelling mound under her fingers.

Damon looked pale, and his mouth was compressed into a thin line.

'I'm taking you to the doctor,' he said, wrapping her into a blanket over her weak protest. 'You were out like a light for a few minutes. There might be something serious.'

'I'm sure there isn't!'

But he put her in the car and tucked her into the back seat with the blanket and a pillow for the long journey.

When they got there Dr James examined her thoroughly

and said that on the whole he concurred with her opinion, but she should rest for a day and Damon was to keep an eye on her.

'I told—my husband there was nothing to worry about,' she said. 'I'm sorry to have taken up your time, Doctor.'

'Not at all,' he said. 'Your husband was very wise to have it checked out. Your father would have insisted—being a doctor himself.'

'My father? Did you know he was—*was* he a doctor?'

'He didn't tell you? Officially, I know nothing, but after I met him, in rather—unusual circumstances, I made some enquiries. Apparently your mother died young of a difficult, obscure disease—difficult to diagnose and difficult to treat. Your father, according to some colleagues who knew him well, felt if his medical knowledge couldn't save her, it was useless, and he stopped practising. Very strange reasoning, in my opinion, but then love often takes people in strange ways.'

'I thought he might have—got into some sort of trouble,' said Rachel. 'Auntie Anne suspected he was a doctor. I know he would never do anything wrong, but perhaps some mistake——'

'Oh, no. By all accounts he was a fine doctor. Pity the profession lost him.'

She was thoughtful on the way home, although she had insisted on sitting in the front passenger seat instead of in the back. Damon glanced anxiously at her from time to time, and when they got home insisted on carrying her in from the car, placing her gently on the bed.

'I'd like a shower,' she said. 'It won't hurt me, Damon, honestly.'

'All right,' he said. 'But leave the bathroom door open. What do you need—this?' He took the towelling robe from the back of the door, and at her nod placed it on the bed. 'What about a nightie?' He bent to open a drawer, and she held her breath as he stared down at the pile of unopened blue airmail envelopes that lay in it.

He didn't look at her, but slammed the drawer shut

again, and she found her voice and said, 'The second drawer.'

He found one and put it by the robe, his face impassive, but not meeting her eyes. 'Is that all?' he asked.

'Yes. Everything else is in the bathroom.'

Rachel had her shower and got into bed, and he brought her sandwiches and a hot drink, but she wasn't hungry and he took away the sandwiches without comment.

To her utter surprise she slept like a log, and woke feeling fine, but Damon insisted on her staying in bed for the day. He tended her with a kind of impersonal gentleness, bringing meals and drinks on a tray and giving her books to read, but after lunch she felt unaccountably sleepy and had a long nap.

When she woke he was standing by the bed, watching her.

She smiled tentatively, and he sat down on the side of the bed and leaned over with his arms on either side of her, to press a gentle kiss on her bruised temple.

'Is it any use saying I'm sorry?' he murmured.

'I tripped,' she said. 'It wasn't your fault.'

'Yes, it was.' He sat back a little. 'If I hadn't been so— brutal with you, it wouldn't have happened.'

She looked down at her hands resting on the bedcover and said, 'Damon, did you really believe those things you said?'

'No.'

She searched his face, wondering how he could have accused her if he knew Des had been lying.

'I was furious with you,' he said. 'But not because I thought Des was your lover.'

Rachel didn't understand, but let it pass, for now. 'I wasn't fighting him, because I'd tried, and it only made him—worse. I was hoping to take him off guard by pretending I'd given up.'

His face grim, Damon said, 'I see. Did you invite him here?'

'Heavens, no! I've always hated him.'

His brows lifted a little. 'Always?'

'Well—ever since——' She sighed and tried as best she could to explain what had happened the previous year.

Damon heard her out without comment, then commented, 'You were a very green little girl, weren't you?'

'In some ways. I've grown up since then.'

'I wonder,' he said enigmatically, and then, 'I'll bring you something to eat.'

She ate alone, but he brought in his cup of coffee afterwards with hers and sat on a straightbacked chair in the corner to drink it.

'Tell me about America,' she invited.

He gave her a slightly sardonic glance, and she supposed he was thinking of his unread letters, but he began to tell her about the places and the people, both famous and obscure, that he had come in contact with. He even told her a little about his work and how it felt to see the film of his own book taking shape. Rachel encouraged him with questions and comments, and he had been talking quite a long time when he mentioned meeting a couple of expatriate New Zealanders. Trying to sound casual, she asked, 'Did you see much of Paula?'

'Paula,' he repeated in a flat tone, his face expressionless.

'She left soon after you did,' she said. Then, defiantly, she added, 'It was in the papers—you surely didn't think I wouldn't *know*?'

She hadn't meant to sound like that—accusing and suspicious, but there was no taking back the words.

Damon got up and took her cup. 'You should have read my letters,' he said, and went out.

CHAPTER FIFTEEN

RACHEL couldn't sleep that night. Listening to the gentle roar of the waves on the beach and the muted cry of a more-pork out in the warm darkness, she wished she had not slept so long that afternoon.

After several restless hours she got up and went to the kitchen for a glass of water. As she put the glass on the bench after rinsing it, Damon appeared in the kitchen doorway, tying a short towelling robe around his waist.

'What's the matter?' he asked.

'I'm all right,' she answered. 'I just can't sleep. I'm sorry I disturbed you. I'll get a book.'

'Would you like a hot drink?'

'No, thanks. A book will help.'

She was wearing her flimsy nightdress, and as his eyes passed over it his mouth twisted with a semblance of bitter humour. 'If our relationship was a little less strained,' he said, 'I might offer you a different remedy.'

Suddenly tempted to forget the questions between them, to take the limited happiness that he was offering, she said softly, 'And I might accept it.'

Tension filled the air between them as his eyes found hers and held them. 'You're pushing your luck, Rachel,' he said softly. 'Supposing I took you up on that?'

'Supposing,' she answered, in a bare whisper, her eyes still bravely meeting his.

She saw the flare of something in his, and heard him say, 'You're under doctor's orders, and I've done enough damage for now.' He turned away, but paused in the doorway to look over his shoulder. 'But some time soon, I might just see if you mean that.'

Rachel crept back into bed, but not to sleep. In the small

hours she got up and trying to do it soundlessly, opened the
drawer containing Damon's letters.

When it was barely dawn she got up and pulled off her
nightgown and shrugged into the short robe behind the
door, creeping out of the house and down to the beach.

The morning sea was almost tranquil, and chill on her
naked body, but soothing and invigorating at the same
time.

When she stood to come out, the sun was slanting early
rays across the water and on to the sand, and Damon was
standing near the water's edge, waiting for her.

This time she made no attempt to hide herself from his
gaze, but walked to him steadily, with her head high, and
let him fold around her the robe she had discarded on the
sand. He was wearing one himself, and had a blanket slung
over one shoulder.

He pulled her with him a few yards up the beach to dry
sand, and began rubbing her down through the towelling
that she clutched in front of her.

'You little idiot!' he said huskily. 'The doctor wouldn't
call an early morning swim resting!'

'He said to rest for a day,' she said. 'I've done that, and
I'm quite all right.'

He pulled the blanket around her shoulders, enveloping
her in it and holding the edges together beneath her chin.

'Are you sure?' he said intently.

'I'm sure—I'm quite recovered.'

Damon said, 'I looked in your room.'

She had left his letters scattered all over the bed. Love-
letters, every one of them.

'I wish I'd read them before,' she said. 'I didn't know
you loved me.'

'How could you not?' he asked, frowning. 'I showed it
every way I knew.'

'Except to say the words.'

'They so often mean so little. And I say the words more
easily in writing.'

Rachel smiled. 'I know. So do I. You know the poems
were for you.'

His hands moved to go around her, pulling her close to him.

'I know. I was simply furious because you wouldn't admit it. Like you, I wanted to be told.'

'And you wanted to punish me for refusing to listen to you about Paula.'

'I suppose—perhaps that, too,' he admitted.

'I'm sorry,' she said, sliding her arms about his neck, and making the blanket slip a little. 'I think Paula *meant* me to think that your affair with her had only ended when you decided to marry me. She told me she couldn't remember afterwards exactly what she said. She's Karina, isn't she? The girl who walked out on you a long time ago.'

'Yes. And walked back in at a most inconvenient time. But believe me, when she came to me just the week before our marriage, after having a row with the man she's been living with for some years, it was only as an old friend. She said she simply had no one else to run to, and she was out of work and had no money. And she didn't use her key that time—she must have been hanging on to it for years. I suppose I should have told her, when I said she couldn't stay, that I was planning to marry. But it seemed a bit like kicking her when she was down.'

'I don't think she's nearly as bad as Karina,' Rachel said thoughtfully. 'I quite like her.'

'You *what*? You unbelievable girl!'

'Why? You—loved her once.'

'Not as I love you. I was young and rather naïve myself, flattered by the attention of a beautiful woman, and I'm afraid I thought it rather classy to have an affair with an actress, too.'

'It must have gone a bit deeper than that.'

Looking down at her grave face, he admitted, 'It did, but not at first. Neither of us was thinking in terms of permanency. And there's no reason for Paula to come between us—you must believe that.'

His hands were caressing her back through the blanket. She said, leaning her head against him, 'Why did you keep telling me that you didn't need to love me to—want me?'

The hands on her back stopped moving. 'I didn't!' he said positively.

Raising her head, she protested, 'But you did! Several times. Even when I asked you point blank why you married me, you—implied it was for sex.'

Baffled, he was thinking. Finally he said, 'I didn't mean that. Men and women have different ways of expressing things—you wanted the words, and I tried to show you, instead, that I loved you. At that moment the words seemed supremely irrelevant.'

'Not to me.'

'No, I see that now. But it seems that when I did try to talk about it, you misunderstood. When I said love wasn't necessary, I meant on *your* side. You said just once that you loved me, and although I knew you were too young to know what you were talking about, I was convinced that if you let me love you, you would come to understand, and learn to trust me.'

'Perhaps I *was* too young then,' she said humbly. Certainly her trust had been weak, and easily broken, a frail thing. 'But I meant it. And I've grown up a lot since then.'

'You have, I know. It shows in those poems.'

Damon's hands slipped under the blanket and she arched herself against him, until the blanket fell to the ground, and he pulled her down on it, spreading it beneath them. Her robe fell open and she saw him looking at her before his mouth murmured against hers, 'My beautiful Aphrodite!'

The waves paced the rhythm of their lovemaking, and her small, smothered cry of pain rose into the sea-scented air and mingled with the calls of the early gulls flying high in the morning. Damon made a muffled exclamation against the soft skin of her neck, and pressed his lips to her flesh in a gesture that she recognised as remorse, as she clutched at his smooth shoulders.

Soon afterwards he rolled off her still body and she felt the warmth of the blanket pulled around her and, strangely, began to shiver. Her eyes were closed, but she knew he was looking down at her.

'Are you all right?' he asked.

Trying to smile, she said, 'Yes.'

'I hurt you.'

'Only a little.'

She felt him gather her into his arms, the blanket still closely folded round her. He kissed her mouth firmly, and the shivering stopped.

She gave a long sigh and opened her eyes. His eyes were concerned and tender.

'I love you,' he said.

He stood up, bringing her with him, and let the blanket fall to the sand as he swung her up in his arms and walked to the water, only letting her find her feet when he was more than waist deep.

The breakers gently buffeted them, but Rachel was steadied against Damon's body, his arms twined about her waist as they stood together, Damon holding her in front of him, her hair floating in tendrils against his shoulder.

Then he asked, 'Want to swim?' And she nodded and floated away from him, but not very far, and they kept touching and smiling at each other, and exchanging brief, salt-tasting kisses as they swam and floated lazily under the pale sun.

They came out hand in hand, and he helped her into her robe before shrugging into his. Then his arms went round her again and he pushed the wet, clinging hair back from her face and gently prised her lips apart with his until they lost the coolness of the sea and warmed into sweet desire.

He released her reluctantly and picked up the blanket, but she rejected it as they went up the narrow path. She felt warm enough, and intensely alive, every inch of her skin tingling with a new awareness.

Damon made her go back to her bed, and brought tea and toast.

She had bundled up his letters and they lay in an untidy heap on top of the chest of drawers.

'Why didn't you read them before?' he asked, as she finished her tea.

'I thought it would hurt too much. I thought they would be letters from a stranger.'

'Was I a stranger to you?'

'Sometimes,' she said huskily. 'Even when you made love to me, it was in anger. How can you make loving a—punishment?'

He took the empty tray from her and put it aside, then sat on the bed, leaning over her to kiss her forehead gently. 'It wasn't anger so much as desperation,' he told her. 'From that disastrous night of our wedding, you seemed to have lost all your feeling for me, and I tried my damnedest to revive it. Even to the point of trying to force you to accept me.'

'Damon——' she hesitated.

'What is it?' His hand stroked her still dampened hair back from her face, and she moved her head a little to feel his knuckles against her cheek.

'What did you mean—when you first offered to take me away? You didn't have marriage in mind, did you?'

'I *always* had marriage in mind, certainly from the time you came to me with your problem over Jerry, and I kissed you until I was nearly out of my mind.'

'*You* were——!'

'Yes,' he admitted ruefully. 'Only I had a little more practice at concealing my feelings than you had. Things went further than I intended, that night—in more ways than one. I finally had to face the fact that I was in love with a girl little more than half my age, who certainly wasn't in love with me—not in any adult way, at any rate. I knew I wanted you for the rest of my life, and that it wasn't fair to ask you to tie yourself to me when you'd had no chance to spread your wings and find out what you really wanted from life.'

'I was too young for you.'

'*I* was too old for *you*, Rachel. It's rather different. When I came back and found how nearly you'd committed yourself to a lifetime with *Jerry*, all I could think of was that you needed to get away. When I said I'd take you, I was still trying hard to be altruistic, but when you put my own real desire into words, and you looked as though you wanted it too, I couldn't help thinking, the hell with being self-sacrificing. I promised myself I wouldn't clip your wings, I'd let you find yourself in every way and grow up properly in your own time, but I wanted your love while you did it.'

'I wanted your love, too,' she said softly. 'I thought it was different for you. I thought—that you saw me as just another of your love affairs.'

He said, 'I haven't had that many, you know. Do you see me as a rake, by any chance?'

Rachel shook her head. 'I thought Karina and Paula were two different women, and that—there'd been others in between.'

Damon looked at her a little aghast, then laughed. 'You still have that idea of a dissolute writer's life, don't you? I'll bet you pictured me in Hollywood, up to my eyes in drink and women!'

'Why did you come back?' she asked.

'Isn't it obvious—I had to see you, to find out why my letters weren't being answered.' His hands gripped her shoulders. 'I was frantic. I humbled myself to you, woman —explained in minute detail about Paula, although I'd sworn I wouldn't unless you *asked* for an explanation—and I threw my very soul at your mercy, in those letters. And not a word from you!'

'That's the first time you've called me a woman,' she said.

His eyes reflected remembered anger and frustration, that changed to lambent passion. 'You are one now,' he said, and began kissing her as though he couldn't help himself.

Rachel lay quiet in his arms, and he raised his head to look into her eyes, darkened and perhaps slightly apprehensive. He smudged his lips over her temples and down to below her ear, and murmured, 'Next time it will be better for you.'

'When is next time?' she asked.

'Whenever you say. Not before.'

He raised his head and began to release her from his tight arms, but she put up her hands and made him look at her, because she wanted to see his face when she said it.

Softly, she told him, 'I say now.'

Harlequin Romances

The books that let you escape into the wonderful world of romance! Trips to exotic places ... interesting plots ... meeting memorable people ... the excitement of love .... These are integral parts of Harlequin Romances — the heartwarming novels read by women everywhere.

Many early issues are now available. Choose from this great selection!

In the Shade of the Palms

On a May Morning

Out of a Dream

A Parade of Peacocks

Choose from this list of Harlequin Romance editions.

Relive a great love story…
Harlequin Romances 1980
Complete and mail this coupon today!

Harlequin Reader Service

In U.S.A.
MPO Box 707
Niagara Falls, N.Y. 14302

In Canada
649 Ontario St.
Stratford, Ontario, N5A 6W2

Please send me the following Harlequin Romance novels. I am enclosing my check or money order for $1.25 for each novel ordered, plus 59¢ to cover postage and handling.

☐ 449	☐ 528	☐ 658	☐ 804	☐ 904	☐ 451
☐ 454	☐ 532	☐ 711	☐ 805	☐ 911	☐ 462
☐ 464	☐ 538	☐ 712	☐ 856	☐ 918	☐ 468
☐ 469	☐ 557	☐ 730	☐ 861	☐ 409	☐ 478
☐ 494	☐ 597	☐ 766	☒ 890	☐ 430	☐ 485
☐ 500	☐ 604	☐ 796	☐ 892	☐ 438	☐ 489
☐ 513	☐ 627	☐ 800	☐ 895	☐ 443	☐ 491
☐ 516	☐ 643	☐ 802	☐ 901	☐ 446	☐ 495

Number of novels checked @ $1.25 each = $_____

N.Y. State residents add appropriate sales tax $_____

Postage and handling $_____.59

TOTAL $_____

I enclose _____
(Please send check or money order. We cannot be responsible for cash sent through the mail.)

Prices subject to change without notice.

NAME _____
(Please Print)

ADDRESS _____

CITY _____

STATE/PROV. _____

ZIP/POSTAL CODE _____

Offer expires September 30, 1980.

0055633

And there's still *more* love in

Harlequin Presents...

Yes!

Six more spellbinding
romantic stories every month
by your favorite authors.
Elegant and sophisticated tales of
love and love's conflicts.

Let your imagination be swept away to
exotic places in search of adventure,
intrigue and romance. Get to
know the warm, true-to-life
characters. Share the special
kind of miracle that
love can be.

Don't miss out. Buy now and discover
the world of HARLEQUIN PRESENTS...

What the press says about Harlequin romance fiction...

"The most popular reading matter of American women today."
— *The Detroit News*

"Women have come to trust these stories about contemporary people, set in exciting foreign places."
— *Best Sellers,* New York

"Harlequin novels have a vast and loyal readership."
— *Toronto Star*